D0064526

TOWARD CLIMATE JUSTICE

BRIAN TOKAR

TOWARD CLIMATE JUSTICE

Perspectives on the Climate Crisis and Social Change

new-compass.net

Toward Climate Justice:
Perspectives on the Climate Crisis and Social Change
2010, 2014 © Brian Tokar

ISBN 978-82-93064-08-4
ISBN 978-82-93064-09-1 (ebook)

Published by New Compass Press
Grenmarsvegen 12
N–3912 Porsgrunn
Norway

Design and layout by Eirik Eiglad

New Compass presents ideas on participatory democracy, social ecology, and movement building—for a free, secular, and ecological society.

new-compass.net
2014

CONTENTS

Foreword

Global warming is the most immediate and vexing ecological challenge facing humanity. Only a few degrees increase in temperature may have far-reaching and dire consequences for biological diversity, ecosystem stability, and human demography.

Since the UN-initiated Intergovernmental Panel on Climate Change (IPCC) published its fourth comprehensive report in 2007, a general acceptance of an impending climate crisis has spread from scientific circles into the mainstream media. Now it is widely acknowledged that not only is our planet faced with the immediate threat of global warming, but that these climate changes are man-made.

The fact that global warming is caused by human activity does not mean that we are all equally to blame. The greenhouse gas emissions from the industrialized "North" have been disproportionate, and continue to be so. Indeed, the countries of the North have to a great extent developed their technological assets and global hegemony precisely through the intensive burning of fossil fuels. Paradoxically, however, the intensification of the climate crisis is likely to have the most devastating effects on people in the impoverished and underdeveloped "South." Globally, the people who have contributed the least to climate-altering emissions will not only be hit hardest by increasing weather chaos and rising sea levels, but are the least prepared technologically to face the ordeals of the coming decades. Therefore, the climate crisis not only poses a challenge to our societies in a general sense, but it also challenges our sense of social justice. There is something fundamentally unfair about the fact that those populations who will be hit the hardest are those least responsible for causing the crisis in the first place. This simple recognition strikes at the heart of the climate justice issue.

As we see it, the issue of global warming and social justice may well prove to be the crucial battle for the ecology movement in the years ahead. A movement for climate justice is bound to touch upon and confront all issues regarding fair distribution, energy use, technology, infrastructure, urban reorganization, and agrarian reform, as well as the reclaiming of the commons and the potential for a participatory politics.

On a superficial level, to be sure, ecological concerns that were rightfully considered politically subversive only decades ago now have become common wisdom. However, in order to properly confront the crises of our time, we need to recover the radical messages of the ecology movement. In an immediate, practical sense, we need to look at what concrete solutions are available from a sustainable, ecological perspective. How can we act swiftly to reduce our societies' dependence on fossil fuels and reduce harmful emissions? On a most practical level, new technologies—as well as more extensive and more efficient use of existing eco-technology— can ameliorate the impact of global warming, and ultimately help reverse the path that we are on.

However, we need to go beyond the very idea that new technologies will solve the ecological crisis. There are no simple solutions and there is no "technical fix." If current political structures and economic imperatives remain intact, we will still have a wasteful and highly energy-demanding— indeed, anti-ecological and unjust—social order. For this reason, there is an urgent need to start defining what the outlines of *an ecological society* will actually look like; our answers to this question will inform how we will make full use of the liberatory potential of new technologies. Arguably it is only in a non-exploitative and liberatory social context that we can assure that the whole of society—on a global scale—will benefit from technological and scientific advances. Indeed, the adaptation of new ecological technologies requires a drastic decentralization of energy use and food production, as well as of infrastructures and political decision-making.

Further, we need to create *a new global ecological movement* able to define the outlines of an ecological society and struggle to actualize it. Such a movement must seek to bridge the economic and political gaps between the North and the South. Indeed, in confronting these issues the ecology movement must become truly global in its perspectives and outreach, and strive to make new bonds between activists all over the world. Importantly, we must work to compensate for the economic disadvantages forced on peasants and producers in the global South. At the same time, such a movement must develop real local political foundations, and strive to bridge the gaps between the rich and the poor in all communities, strengthen municipal political life, encourage regional ecological production, and foster communal sensibilities—by empowering common people as responsible *citizens.*

To fulfill the promises of climate justice we need to ask ourselves even more questions. How can we see beyond the current environmental focus on the major climate summits (like COP 15 in Copenhagen and COP 16 in Cancún), important as they may be, and understand why they have failed to take decisive action? How can we discern and expose the fashionable "false solutions" propagated by the profit-hungry corporations and their lobbies? What can we learn from the escalated calls for climate justice, and how can we act accordingly? How can we work to strengthen this global movement, and make sure it lives up to its far-reaching ideals? And what may this movement learn from the theory and practice of social ecology? Brian Tokar touches upon all these questions, and more, in this book.

Brian Tokar is a seasoned activist with a long commitment to peace, justice and environmental concerns. Tokar was introduced to radical activism in New York City in the early 1970s, first in anti-war work, and then in the powerful antinuclear movement. In 1980, inspired by the ideas of social ecologist Murray Bookchin, he moved to Vermont to work with the Institute for Social Ecology (ISE), and got increasingly involved in Green politics and environmental justice. Tokar has been a key coordinator of resistance against biotechnology and genetic engineering in New England, and he founded the ISE's Climate Justice Project in 2006. He is currently the director of the ISE and an instructor in environmental studies at the University of Vermont.

Brian Tokar's authorship reflects this engagement with radical ecology, and his major publications include *The Green Alternative: Creating an Ecological Future* (San Pedro: R. & E. Miles, 1987; Revised edition 1992), and *Earth for Sale: Reclaiming Ecology in the Age of Corporate Greenwash* (Boston: South End Press, 1997). Tokar has also edited books such as *Redesigning Life? The Worldwide Challenge to Genetic Engineering* (London: Zed Books, 2001), and *Gene Traders: Biotechnology, World Trade, and the Globalization of Hunger* (Burlington: Toward Freedom, 2004). His most recent book on food politics, edited with Fred Magdoff, is titled *Agriculture and Food in Crisis: Conflict, Resistance, and Renewal* (New York: Monthly Review, 2010). These publications all point to Tokar's long-standing involvement with the ecology movement. Tokar also has written numerous essays and articles throughout the decades, engaging with the pressing environmental issues of the day.

The original edition of *Toward Climate Justice* (2010) was substantially based on a series of essays that first appeared in various journals. The author and publishers would like to thank the editors of *Z Magazine*, the *Journal of Aesthetics and Protest*, *Communalism: A Social Ecology Journal*, *Capitalism Nature Socialism*, the websites *ZNet*, *Counterpunch*, *Toward Freedom* and *AlterNet*, and (for this revised edition) the *Routledge Handbook of the Climate Change Movement* for originally publishing those essays, portions of which were adapted and reworked for this volume. Brian Tokar's essays have aimed to explain, encourage, and influence the emerging climate justice movement since early 2008. Now thoroughly updated and revised, this book seeks to offer a comprehensive overview of the movement and its challenges.

While ecological concerns today are publicly acknowledged and debated, mainstream media tend to go to great lengths to downplay their radical underlying messages. Still, the intensifying climate crisis—with its prospects for global warming and meteorological chaos—requires creative social alternatives as well as bold political action. As a social ecologist, Brian Tokar urges us to go to the roots of the ecological crisis and propose new social alternatives. That such solutions are needed is an understatement.

It remains, however, to see whether this emerging movement for climate justice will succeed in bridging the economic and political gaps between the North and the South—the affluent and the impoverished—into a new responsible politics for civic empowerment and global solidarity. But this movement aspires to do so, and we all need to help it live up to its potential.

Our choices and actions today—for better or worse—will have defining consequences for future generations.

Eirik Eiglad
June 2010

Preface to the Revised Edition

J ust a few short years ago, as the research for this book was beginning to take shape, public discussions of the emerging global climate crisis were far different than today's. Global warming was generally depicted as an esoteric scientific issue with impacts that would be felt in a somewhat distant future. Efforts to engage the public, especially in the United States, were generally limited to explaining the science of global warming and emphatically making the case that the phenomenon was real. Environmentalists embraced images of polar bears stranded on shrinking ice floes, and occasionally referenced the experiences of island dwellers concerned about the loss of their homes to rising sea levels. For the most part, climate issues were something for future generations to grapple with. For the present, people could be consumed with more immediate concerns.

Now we have unambiguously entered the age of extreme weather. Unprecedented droughts, storms and wildfires are almost constantly in the news, even in the relatively sheltered communities of North America. Uniquely powerful hurricanes and tornadoes have devastated communities throughout the East and South, and unprecedented droughts and wildfires continually plague the West. Images of devastating storm damage from other parts of the world paint an even more severe image of our current reality. While mainstream commentators persist in attributing such incidents to short-term weather phenomena like El Niño currents and polar vortices, it is clear that something has dramatically shifted in our day-to-day experience of life on this planet. When established authors on climate change like James Hansen and Bill McKibben write that today's earth no longer resembles the one on which civilizations emerged, it is not merely an artistic flourish, but a central fact of our daily lived experience.

The relationship between extreme weather and longer-term, human-induced changes to the global climate remains an area of legitimate scientific controversy. The underlying processes are complex, and it's difficult to be sure about the links between climate and weather, even as we are now effectively certain that human activities such as burning fossil fuels and cutting down the world's forests are disrupting the climate system and warming the earth. But a few things are well understood.

First, warm air simply holds more moisture, a straight-forward physical phenomenon. In a warming climate, clouds accumulate more water over a longer period of time and have more water to unload when conditions are finally ripe for rainfall. The 2014 US National Climate Assessment reports that a consistently higher proportion of precipitation now falls in the form of very heavy storms, up to a 71 percent increase in the northeastern US from 20th century norms.[1]

Secondly, we know that the turbulent weather we are experiencing is precisely what increasingly sophisticated models of the global climate have long predicted. The entire system is shifting ever farther from the relatively stable state that prevailed for much of human history—over hundreds, and likely thousands, of years. The current instability of Arctic and Antarctic ice is one key indicator. Climatologist James Hansen describes these shifts in the climate as analogous to playing a game with loaded dice. For quite a long time, the odds of relatively normal temperature, below normal temperature, and above normal temperature were about equal, as if each of these conditions were represented by two sides of a six-sided cube. To portray today's realities, the cube-shaped dice would have to be reimagined, such that four of the six sides represent warmer than normal conditions, and more than half a "side" (to stretch the analogy somewhat) would have to represent weather that is statistically far warmer than normal.[2] As of this writing, twenty nine years have passed since the world as a whole last experienced a single month that averaged below normal in temperature by 20th century standards.[3] These observations, given the parallel and consistent predictions of climate models, strengthen the case that extreme weather is significantly attributable to the shifting climate.

Finally, a few studies have sought to measure the specific role of climate change in causing individual extreme weather events. One of the most detailed studies, which appeared in the prestigious journal *Nature* in early 2011, sought to measure how much climate changes contributed to a series of catastrophic flooding events in England and Wales during the autumn of 2000. The study took ten years to complete and mobilized a vast network of volunteers to offer surplus time on their home and office computers in order to run thousands of forecast scenarios and complete the required calculations. In the end, the researchers determined that anthropogenic greenhouse gas emissions made those severe storms 90 percent more likely in two out of three climate model scenarios. In 90 percent of scenarios, the severity of the storms was at least 20% attributable to greenhouse gases. Such precision is technically possible, but in fact only serves to confirm the conclusions that climate scientists have been discussing in more general terms for a very long time.[4]

Another important factor that has changed dramatically since the chapters of this book first began to be drafted during 2007-09 is the character of the climate change movement.[5] From 2007 onward, representatives of civil society organizations have converged annually at the site of various UN climate negotiations, seeking to urge stronger global policies to curtail excess emissions of carbon dioxide and other greenhouse gases. Many representatives of indigenous and other land-based peoples from around the world have made a compelling case that the climate crisis is not just another environmental issue, but one with profound implications for human rights and human survival. This is especially true for the most marginalized communities in the global South, who have been experiencing the consequences of extreme weather and a destabilized climate for well over a decade.

In the lead-up to the 2009 climate summit in Copenhagen, the new "350.org" network began staging symbolic but highly visible demonstrations around the world to dramatize the need to stabilize atmospheric carbon dioxide at 350 parts per million. These were relatively early, somewhat cautious stirrings of a rising public awareness of the severity of the climate crisis. In Copenhagen itself, as many as 100,000 people took to the streets to demand a comprehensive global climate agreement that was not to be. But after a short hiatus, concerned people around the world are again on the march, and the contrast is especially noteworthy in the US. A thousand people were arrested outside the White House in the late summer of 2012 protesting the proposed Keystone XL oil pipeline and nearly 40,000 demonstrated in Washington in the winter of 2014. As of this writing, a significantly larger public event was being planned in New York City to coincide with a special meeting called by UN Secretary General Ban Ki Moon to urge heads of state to make good on the promise of a new international climate agreement by 2015.

Even more significantly, people around the world have been organizing to resist what the *New York Times* has called the largest expansion of fossil fuel infrastructure since the 1950s. With readily accessible sources of oil and gas reaching their limits worldwide, fossil fuel producers are going to great lengths to tap into so-called "unconventional" sources of oil and gas—such as tar sands, previously impenetrable shale formations, and oil deposits lying miles beneath the oceans, including in the far reaches of the Arctic. Michael Klare, a long-time analyst of energy geopolitics, describes this as the age of "extreme energy," as most new sources of oil and gas now require energy companies "to drill in extreme temperatures or extreme weather, or use extreme pressures, or operate under extreme danger—or some combination of all of these."[6] Extreme energy extraction is far more threatening to ecosystems and human communities than conventional oil drilling, and the organized opposition of those communities has significantly reshaped the climate movement's understanding of the local impacts of climate-destroying activities.[7]

In recent years, we have seen a widespread uprising of First Nations indigenous communities across Canada, objecting to the exceptionally destructive extraction of oil from the Alberta Tar Sands, as well as the construction of new and expanded pipelines across the continent to facilitate exports of tar sands bitumen. Opposition to hydraulic fracturing ("fracking") of underground shale formations to extract oil and gas has arisen throughout North America, as well as in the UK, Eastern Europe, and as far afield as South Africa. Iñupiat communities in Alaska have been at the forefront of opposition to oil drilling in newly navigable but uniquely hazardous Arctic waters, and environmentalists everywhere breathed a sigh of relief when Shell Oil withdrew its damaged drilling vessels from Alaskan waters in early 2013.[8] In the historic coal mining regions of the eastern US an unprecedented alliance of long-time local residents and youthful forest activists seeks to end the most extreme form of strip-mining for coal, appropriately described as "mountaintop-removal" mining.[9] All these developments speak to the potential for a heightened sense of immediacy in today's climate movements, and an increased awareness of the energy industry's local, as well as global impacts.

The core underlying message of climate justice—that those who contribute least to excess greenhouse gas emissions are disproportionately impacted by climate changes—is now embraced by a wide variety of distinct but complementary popular movements from around the world. The most urgent voices continue to be those of indigenous and other land-based peoples, especially in the global South, whose communities have felt the impacts of climate disruptions that threaten their lands and their entire way of life. In the North, climate justice has continued the evolution of a variety of global justice movements that emerged in response to the rise of international financial institutions such as the World Trade Organization during the late 1990s and early 2000s. This includes the youthful Rising Tide network, which was founded in Europe, sprouted chapters throughout the US, Canada and Australia, and has staged dramatic direct actions to challenge numerous false solutions to the climate crisis, as well as the expansion of extreme energy. In the US, the leading voices for climate justice are often from communities of color that have been organizing for decades in response to their disproportionate exposure to a wide variety of environmental hazards. These environmental justice communities continue the legacy of the civil rights movement in the US as they resist environmental racism and seek a transition to a more just and sustainable future. This unique constellation of voices from around the world has proved central to our understanding of the profound social justice and human rights implications of the unfolding climate crisis.

In conventional environmental policy circles, however, very little has changed since this book first appeared in 2010. Significant numbers of environmental policy advocates continue to accept inadequate and short-sighted approaches to curtailing climate-related pollution in the name of a misdirected political "realism." International negotiators at the UN level continue to advance the notion of "voluntary" national pledges as the most viable way to achieve global reductions of greenhouse gases, and policymakers persist in implementing proposed reductions through the market-based trading of carbon emissions allowances. The focus on emissions trading contributed greatly to the failings of the 1997 Kyoto Protocol, as we will see, and remains a central focus of climate policy discussions in the US and Europe, including the Obama administration's latest efforts to reduce emissions from coal-fired power plants.

Energy industries and policymakers continue to persist in promoting numerous false solutions to the climate crisis. Not only carbon markets, but also various forms of large-scale experimentation with the atmosphere—termed "geoengineering"—are actively promoted by those who are unwilling to consider the necessary changes to energy production and the structures of the economic system. Environmentally destructive and uncertain energy technologies, including nuclear power, carbon sequestration from coal plants, and the large scale combustion of biomass for energy, are widely depicted as part of the solution rather than as merely perpetuating existing problems. The expansion of hydraulic fracturing of shale formations as a means to extract previously unreachable deposits of oil and gas has served to reinforce the long-standing myth that natural gas can serve as a "bridge fuel" to a more sustainable future.

The use of more genuinely renewable energy sources is also growing rapidly, but its course of development under a system of corporate control and financial speculation has raised many questions of its own. Many analysts point out that power from the sun and wind are now the fastest growing energy sources, surpassing new fossil fuel projects in much of the US and Europe. Countries like Denmark, Spain, Portugal and Germany are in the forefront, and even some US states are approaching 20 percent renewable electricity. But these projects still represent a small fraction of overall consumption, and many renewables are adding to, rather than replacing, existing capacity. Community controlled models of wind power development, as pioneered in Denmark, are increasingly superseded by larger, corporate-owned projects, raising heightened concerns over the impacts on ecosystems and communities, even in regions where support for climate mitigation measures is strong.

We know that technologies exist to meet our essential needs with far less energy, and to permit a conversion to non-fossil, non-nuclear energy sources by mid-century or sooner.[10] The main obstacles, as we shall see, are the entrenched political power of the fossil fuel industries, their continued excessive profitability as prices rise, and the widespread disinterest in renewable energy on the part of global capital. Questions about future energy sources are, above all, questions about what kind of society we want to live in, a topic we will return to in this book's later chapters.

Readers familiar with the original 2010 edition of this book may notice rather substantial changes and revisions on nearly every page. I've attempted to update every chapter with new information and analysis on recent developments in climate science and politics. The most substantial changes are in Chapters 3 and 4. Chapter 3 incorporates the discussion of the origins of climate justice that originally appeared in Chapter 2, and includes material from three other articles I've written since 2012 chronicling the climate justice movement. Chapter 4, on carbon markets and the other corporate-driven false solutions to the climate crisis, combines portions of the original chapters 2 and 4 and updates the story of the evolution of US climate policies.

Whereas the first three chapters of the original book were largely based on a series of magazine articles that reviewed the broad scope of developments in climate justice over a period of years, leading up to the UN conference in Copenhagen and its immediate aftermath, I believe the new chapters 1-4 are all substantially more coherent and topical, each now addressing a specific aspect of the evolving climate justice story. The last two chapters are substantially unchanged in structure (except for the removal of the false solutions discussions from Chapter 5), though a summary of my further research on current utopian thought—a portion of which was added to the social ecology chapter at the last moment in 2010—is now placed where it properly belongs in Chapter 5.

I am grateful to my students at the University of Vermont for their thoughtful comments and questions on these chapters over the past few years, and especially to Rachel Smolker, who reviewed drafts of the revised chapters and offered her incomparable insights and suggestions. Eirik Eiglad of The New Compass has demonstrated an exceptional patience and diligence throughout the many stages of this project. I also credit the unfailing energy and inspiration of my colleagues on the board of 350Vermont and the youthful activists of Rising Tide Vermont for helping sustain my confidence that we *can* create a better world.

Brian Tokar
East Montpelier, Vermont
June 2014

1

Global Warming and the Struggle for Justice

How can we give voice to a more justice-centered approach to the global climate crisis? This question was raised by activists from around the world during the lead-up to the landmark 2009 UN climate conference in Copenhagen, Denmark. As calls for climate justice rang through the streets of Copenhagen that chilly December, both participants and careful observers came to discover the vastly disproportionate human impacts of global climate changes. Until relatively recently, the warming of the earth's climate was most often viewed as a rather esoteric scientific concern, with consequences that would be felt at some indefinite future time and mostly affect the non-human inhabitants of remote and uniquely endangered ecosystems. The most iconic symbol of the wave of climate activism that flourished prior to Copenhagen was the polar bear, struggling to stand its ground amidst shrinking ice flows in the Arctic north.

As tens of thousands of people converged in Copenhagen, a different kind of climate movement had already begun to emerge. While some activists still featured polar bears in their imagery, and many others aimed quite sensibly to focus the world's attention on the need to reduce the atmospheric concentration of carbon dioxide to a maximum of 350 parts per million, a far more urgent outlook on the climate crisis was gradually beginning to capture the world's attention. The outlook known as climate justice is rooted in vulnerable communities around the world that have for many years experienced severe and destabilizing climate-related disruptions to their lives and livelihoods. As we will see, climate justice embodies the fundamental understanding that those who contribute the least to the excess of carbon dioxide and other greenhouse gases in the earth's atmosphere consistently and disproportionately experience the most severe and disruptive consequences of global warming, and are often the least prepared to cope with its consequences.

In the United States, a marked shift in public perceptions was experienced briefly in 2005-06, when Hurricane Katrina flooded New Orleans, and hundreds of thousands of people were forced to flee their homes. Many residents of the most impoverished neighborhoods were left behind in the floods; others were never able to return. Soon afterward, the success of Al Gore's award-winning documentary, *An Inconvenient Truth*, spurred some substantive changes in public attitudes toward global climate disruptions, but the film advocated only the most superficial and shallow solutions, symbolized by the huge new wave of green products and corporate greenwashing that emerged during the late 2000s. In 2007, the UN's Intergovernmental Panel on Climate Change (IPCC) declared the evidence for human-caused global warming "unequivocal," and the disturbing, and sometimes catastrophic, reality of worldwide climate disruptions was beginning to affect many people's daily lives, even in the earth's hitherto sheltered temperate zones.

For much of the 1980s and nineties, the minds of a media-dazzled American public seemed to be firmly lodged in the sand with respect to the emerging changes in the global climate. But by the end of the first decade of the 21st century, disturbing changes in our weather and in the once-familiar patterns of the seasons had become difficult to ignore. Initially, the changes were subtle. Spring would begin a couple of weeks or more earlier than it used to, and fall would start later. Unseasonably warm weather would appear sporadically throughout the year, while cold spells were more sudden, severe, and relatively short-lived. Rainfall in some areas increased markedly, while in other regions it became increasingly sparse, and arrived more often in rapid, concentrated deluges, often accompanied by catastrophic flooding.

These were noticeable, but far from catastrophic changes, making it easier for Americans to remain oblivious to what was happening in other parts of the world. The catastrophic European heat wave of 2003, which killed more than 50,000 people, was barely reported in the US news media, and massive flooding in Pakistan, Indonesia and elsewhere was almost never reported as a climate-related story. Even unprecedented droughts and wildfires, from the Great Plains of the upper Midwest to much of the US southern tier, from Georgia through Texas and Arizona, were generally attributed to short-term weather patterns such the tropical ocean current known as El Niño. When parts of Alabama and Tennessee experienced their driest weather in over a century during 2007, and summer temperatures in Arizona—as well as in parts of Greece and Turkey—reached well above 115 degrees Fahrenheit, or around 45 Celsius, it still was difficult to find broadly accessible discussions of the longer-term climatic significance of these events.

Climate denialism thrived in the US even as wildfires swept repeatedly through large, populated areas of Arizona and southern California, and most media outlets barely mentioned that the hurricanes that devastated New Orleans and surroundings in 2005 were intensified by anomalously high sea temperatures in the Gulf of Mexico and across the South Atlantic. Even when the reality of the unfolding climate crisis did briefly appear to break through the veils of the corporate media, it was quickly superseded by the severe economic downturn that began in 2008 and even by the sensationalized accusations of scientific misconduct that were disingenuously termed "Climate-gate."[1] Weather and climate stories made the news again in 2012 when vast reaches of the agricultural Midwest experienced a dry spell that rivaled the catastrophic "Dust Bowl" years of the 1930s, and just a few months later when the remnants of Hurricane Sandy devastated coastal communities in New York, New Jersey and other eastern states. Climate concerns were raised once again in light of the unprecedented drought and wildfires that swept across California two years later. But these stories, too, were soon swept aside by other world events. An unusually cold, snowy winter throughout the northeastern quarter of the US in 2014—partly attributed to climate-related disruptions of the polar jet stream—further aroused the voices of sarcasm and dismissal: "You call this global warming?"

For people from the Arctic to the subtropics, however, the reality of global climate disruptions has already become an undeniable part of their lived experience. On every continent, the incidence of catastrophic floods, droughts and wildfires has systematically risen. Indigenous Arctic communities experiencing the loss of permafrost and the populations of island nations facing saltwater intrusions from rising seas all face an increasingly imminent need to relocate. Crop failures are increasingly frequent occurrences in many parts of Africa and south Asia, and catastrophic floods have washed away neighborhoods in Jakarta, Bangkok and other major world cities. A persistent and unrelenting drought has contributed greatly to the mass exodus of over a hundred thousand refugees from the continuing political instability in Somalia. The most severe typhoon ever to reach landfall devastated several Philippine islands, right on the eve of the 2013 UN climate conference in Warsaw. While it is a very long and labor-intensive process to precisely measure the climate component of specific weather events, the trends toward more extreme weather consistently match the projections of detailed climate models. It is also clear that these events continue to disproportionately impact indigenous and other land-based communities, as well as poor urban dwellers, and especially the roughly half of the world's population that currently lives on less than two dollars a day.

The inability of many people in the North to comprehend the links between extreme weather and long-term changes in the climate is partly a result of the organized climate change denial that is both directly and indirectly supported by corporate benefactors from the fossil fuel industry.[2] But it is also the result of a persistent failure on the part of those who regularly communicate to the mainstream public about global warming. Until very recently, the climate crisis has been discussed in the US and Europe as mainly a scientific or technical matter. The hazards may be severe, but are viewed as uncertain and long-range in nature. We can read at length about the optimal level of carbon dioxide in the atmosphere and its correlation to predicted changes in average global temperature, but still considerably less about the persistent real-world effects of climate disruptions. The proposed solutions tend to vary from relatively trivial suggestions like changing light bulbs—as highlighted at the end of Gore's 2006 film—to disastrous technical fixes like reviving nuclear power, or pumping sun-blocking particulates into the atmosphere. Few commentators address the underlying systemic roots of the problem, much less the need for a sweeping ecological transformation of society.

The persistent framing of the climate crisis as mainly a scientific problem contributed to the disproportionate coverage of the so-called "Climate-gate" scandals on both sides of the Atlantic. While mounting scientific evidence continues to support the most pessimistic predictions for the future of the earth's climate, leaked emails from British climate scientists and a minor error of interpretation in the IPCC's 2007 report came to dominate the headlines, just as world leaders were getting ready to attend the climate conference in Copenhagen. While it is easy to pin the blame entirely on the corporate-controlled media, the public response has revealed a profound lack of understanding of the nature of scientific uncertainty and the very nature of scientific debate.

In January of 2010, researchers from Yale and George Mason Universities released the results of a detailed survey of public opinions on global warming in the United States, and their findings are disturbing. They found that twice as many Americans believed that global warming was *not* happening, compared to two years earlier (20 percent, compared to only 10 percent in 2008), and that nearly a quarter of the population said they don't know. Only 47 percent of those surveyed said that global warming is caused mainly by human activities, 40 percent believed "there is a lot of disagreement among scientists about whether or not global warming is happening," and only 28 percent (down from 38 percent in 2008) said they thought global warming was already harming people around the world.[3] The BBC reported that barely 26 percent of people in the UK in 2012 accepted that climate change is happening and "largely manmade," and a poll conducted by *Der Spiegel* found that fear of global warming in Germany fell from 62 percent to only 42 percent over a period of four years.[4] While climate concerns, as documented by the Yale group and others, have slowly returned to 2007 levels, political polarization around global warming has also increased, especially in the United States. A more recent report from the Yale and George Mason researchers showed that over 60 percent of Americans support either a large or medium-scale effort to reduce climate change, with proportionate economic costs.[5] However, when US opinion is broken down along lines of political affiliation, two-thirds of self-identified Democrats are very concerned about the issue, compared with just over a quarter of self-identified Republicans.[6]

Even a brief review of the actual data, however, leaves little doubt that disturbing patterns of atmospheric heating, highly erratic weather, and cycles of floods and drought are being felt worldwide. These observations closely match the projections of climate modelers going back more than a decade, and recent warming trends can only be rationally explained if human-induced climate changes are taken into account. The 2013 report of the Intergovernmental Panel on Climate Change showed that this is true for each of the world's continents and oceans, not just the global average temperature.[7] Interestingly, scientists once predicted that many of the climate changes that we are seeing today would only occur several decades farther into the future.

Several systematic studies, most notably the reports of the IPCC's second Working Group, which focuses on the consequences of climate change, have begun to map out this latter story in detail, as we will see shortly. Furthermore, impoverished people around the world are also bearing the consequences of the most prevalent false solutions to global warming, including the push for biofuels, expanded gas drilling, and the global market in carbon offsets. A basic concern for justice and equity today leads irrevocably to the conclusion that a thoroughgoing social and economic transformation is necessary if we are to head off the very worst consequences of an increasingly erratic, overheating climate. While business-as-usual scenarios for future energy use and carbon dioxide emissions are often acknowledged to be untenable, so too is the continuation of business-as-usual in the structure of our political and economic institutions.

Who is affected by global warming?

Since the first Earth Day, close to 45 years ago, there has been a serious divide between those who view environmental issues as fundamentally social and political, and those who focus entirely on the technical aspects of individual problems and on narrow, status-quo solutions. Regulatory agencies and most traditional environmental groups view ecological problems as primarily technical in nature, typically ignoring the larger picture.

As social ecologists have argued since the mid-1960s, however, environmental problems not only have serious human consequences, but are thoroughly social and political in origin.[8] With respect to global climate disruptions, this contrast is now central to understanding where we are and where we may be headed. An understanding of the science and politics of global warming is increasingly shaping how we understand problems of social justice, or war and peace, and how these concerns will play out in the coming decades. A brief look at the evidence should help illuminate this.

One of the first news reports to bring the global justice consequences of global warming to a wide US audience was an insightful piece in the *New York Times* that appeared fast on the heels of the landmark 2007 report of the Intergovernmental Panel on Climate Change. As reporter Andrew Revkin stated, "In almost every instance, the people most at risk from climate change live in countries that have contributed the least to the atmospheric buildup of carbon dioxide and other greenhouse gases linked to the recent warming of the planet. Those most vulnerable countries also tend to be the poorest."[9]

The *Times* dispatched reporters to cover four widely varying instances of people coping with the consequences of a severely altered climate, illustrating some stark contrasts across different parts of the world. In a village in Malawi, officials struggle to maintain the functioning of a simple weather station, chronically lacking basic supplies like light bulbs and chart paper, while in India, rural villagers can barely cope with the effects of more erratic monsoons and increased flooding on their already fragile life support systems. Meanwhile, Western Australia has built a state-of-the-art water desalinization plant, powered by an array of wind turbines about 100 miles away, and the Dutch have begun building homes attached to huge columns that allow the actual houses to rise and fall by as much as 18 feet with the ebb and flow of tidal waters.

The plight of people in various low-lying Pacific island nations has also attracted some mainstream press attention. With rising sea levels, not only are people having to relocate homes away from the shore, but sources of essential drinking water are becoming brackish due to increasing infiltrations of sea water. Migration of Pacific islanders to New Zealand has quadrupled in recent years, according to *The Independent* in the UK, as rising numbers of island communities are becoming uninhabitable.[10] Yet island nations, according to the IPCC, are collectively responsible for far less than 1 percent of global greenhouse gas emissions. In mid-2009, the *New York Times'*

Sunday magazine featured a striking profile of the diplomatic efforts by then-President Mohamed Nasheed of the Maldives to secure a new permanent home for the islands' population.[11]

Closer to home, Hurricane Katrina first highlighted the extreme inequity in people's capacity to cope with climate-related disasters. While affluent homes were mostly restored, and travelers soon returned to New Orleans' unique tourist quarters, roughly a third of the city's population were unable to return home, and emptied public housing projects were threatened with demolition, despite a relatively low level of storm-related damage. While the human toll from the 2007-08 San Diego area wildfires was comparatively low, the systemic inequities were harsh. Naomi Klein reported in *The Nation* in late 2007 that residents able to pay several tens of thousands of dollars were whisked away to elite resorts to wait out the fires, while their homes were sprayed with special fire retardants that were tragically unavailable to their neighbors.[12]

During the same period, however, reports from Bangladesh to the Sudan revealed how climate instability is exacerbating conflict and even bloodshed among people. Droughts in East Africa have caused wells to dry up and livestock to perish, fueling interethnic conflicts among the region's pastoral communities.[13] In India, widespread crop failures due to more frequent droughts and catastrophic flooding events have intensified the tragic wave of farmer suicides that was first brought on by the widespread failure of chemical pesticides and genetically engineered seeds.[14] Half of India's agricultural districts faced persistent drought during the 2009 monsoon season, with crop losses up to 60 percent.[15] The UK-based Environmental Justice Foundation has reported a finding by the UN Convention to Combat Desertification that, in Africa alone, an estimated 10 million people have been displaced or forced to migrate due to environmental degradation and desertification.[16] While the specific climate contribution to particular weather events is still a subject of legitimate scientific debate, three things are clear: 1) Warmer air holds more moisture, thus prolonging periods of drought, as well as the intensity of storms; 2) Chaotic and extreme weather is consistent with the projections of global climate models; and 3) when scientists do commit the time and the extraordinary computing power necessary to calculate the climate component of particular events, the results are generally quite compelling.[17] And along with especially catastrophic events come countless incidents of mis-timing: rain that falls when farmers need and expect it the least; flowers that open weeks before their pollinators arrive, or before they are safe from frost; unanticipated heat-waves in the early spring.

Projections and Realities

In 2007, the Intergovernmental Panel on Climate Change—originally established by the UN Environment Program and the World Meteorological Organization—issued their fourth comprehensive review of climate science. For the first time, the IPCC stated that "warming of the climate system is unequivocal," and that rises in global temperature can only be explained with reference to human-induced increases in carbon dioxide and other so-called "greenhouse gases"—especially methane, nitrous oxide, and the banned but persistent CFCs used in air conditioners and refrigerators.

For the first time, the statistical confidence level of many of their calculations came in at better than 95 percent.[18]

The IPCC documented an unprecedented convergence of findings from hundreds of studies and tens of thousands of distinct data sets in numerous independent fields of inquiry. This feat of scientific data gathering and assessment may have been worthy of a Nobel science prize if the panel hadn't already been awarded the coveted prize for peace in 2007, along with Al Gore. Perhaps never before had scientific studies in so many distinct areas of research converged on one disturbing conclusion: not only that the evidence for the role of human activity in altering the earth's climate is "unequivocal," but that the ecological and human consequences of those alterations are already being felt in countless different ways.

The IPCC's report appeared in three separate volumes published by distinct international Working Groups, plus a concluding Synthesis Report, all released over the course of 2007; the panel's earlier reports, and their fifth assessment report published in 2013-14, are similarly organized. Most media coverage tends to focus on the first volume, examining the physical science basis for climate change. Here the assembled scientists describe the evidence for anthropogenic warming and evaluate a wide range of future greenhouse gas emission scenarios.

Scientists such as James Hansen—now retired from NASA and one of the most widely quoted senior scientists of our time—argue that the IPCC tends to underestimate a variety of factors that negatively affect human populations, including the likely sea level rises. Hansen's analyses in recent years have led to some very alarming conclusions: that a sensible extrapolation from past climate data suggests a sea level rise of up to 80 feet if we don't stop burning fossil fuels, and that with an atmospheric carbon dioxide concentration around 400 parts per million, we've already surpassed the historic carbon dioxide level that is compatible with year-round ice in the Arctic or Antarctic.[19] For Hansen and many others, the question is literally whether or not our earth will continue to resemble the world in which human civilizations have developed, and the only way to accomplish this is to leave most of the remaining fossil fuels in the ground. Meanwhile, policy analysts are proposing "acceptable" or "realistic" greenhouse gas levels that approach 450 or even 550 parts per million.

What often gets lost in these long-term projections, however, are the ways that chaotic global warming is already affecting people around the world today. The IPCC wrote about this in its second Working Group reports in 2007 and 2014, specifically addressing the environmental and human consequences of climate change. But scientists and advocates alike seem to prefer to debate the quantitative details rather than address the ways that our survival is imperiled by the over-consumption of the world's affluent minority.

Most poor people live in the earth's tropical and subtropical regions. They are already living in a world of increasingly uncertain rainfall, persistent droughts, coastal flooding, loss of wetlands and fisheries, and increasingly scarce fresh water supplies. The IPCC confirmed in 2007 that severely increased flooding will most immediately affect residents of the major river deltas of Asia and Africa. Additionally, the one sixth of the world's population that depends on water from glacial runoff may see a brief increase in the size and volume of their freshwater lakes as glaciers melt, but eventually the loss of the glaciers will become a life-threatening reality.[20]

The data points toward a worldwide decrease in crop productivity if global temperatures rise more than 5 degrees Fahrenheit (about 3°C), although crop yields from rain-fed agriculture could be reduced by half as soon as 2020. In Africa alone, between 75 million and 250 million people will be exposed to "increased water stress," according to the IPCC. Agricultural lands in Latin America will be subject to desertification and increasing salt content.

Probably the grimmest tale is contained in the 2007 report's chapter on health consequences of climate changes, which predicted "increases in malnutrition and consequent disorders…; increased deaths, disease and injury due to heatwaves, floods, storms, fires and droughts; the increased burden of diarrheal disease; the increased frequency of cardio-respiratory diseases due to higher concentrations of ground-level ozone…; and, the altered spatial distribution of some infectious disease vectors," including malaria. There is little doubt that those populations with "high exposure, high sensitivity and/or low adaptive capacity" will bear the greatest burdens; those who contribute the least to the problem of global warming will continue to face the most severe consequences.[21]

It took a fair amount of reading between the lines of the IPCC's fourth assessment report, issued in 2007, to find the evidence supporting a climate justice outlook. But by the time of the IPCC's fifth assessment in 2014, the second working group report, focused on climate "impacts, adaptation and vulnerability," was much more thoroughly devoted to the social justice implications of the climate crisis. Six out of the eight "key risks" highlighted in that report's official summary, all identified with high statistical confidence based on the available research literature, strongly affirm the core messages of climate justice and the urgency of justice-centered solutions:

- Risk of death, injury, ill-health, or disrupted livelihoods in low-lying coastal zones and small island developing states and other small islands, due to storm surges, coastal flooding, and sea-level rise.
- Risk of severe ill-health and disrupted livelihoods for large urban populations due to inland flooding in some regions.
- Systemic risks due to extreme weather events leading to breakdown of infrastructure networks and critical services such as electricity, water supply, and health and emergency services.
- Risk of mortality and morbidity during periods of extreme heat, particularly for vulnerable urban populations and those working outdoors in urban or rural areas.
- Risk of food insecurity and the breakdown of food systems linked to warming, drought, flooding, and precipitation variability and extremes, particularly for poorer populations in urban and rural settings.
- Risk of loss of rural livelihoods and income due to insufficient access to drinking and irrigation water and reduced agricultural productivity, particularly for farmers and pastoralists with minimal capital in semi-arid regions.[22]

The entire section concludes with the statement: "Many key risks constitute particular challenges for the least developed countries and vulnerable communities, given their limited ability to cope." Even though the framing in terms of quantifiable risk can serve to distance the discussion from the actual experiences of people living with these hazards, it represents a significant breakthrough in the scientific community's validation of the messages that have emerged from climate justice movements around the world.

Numerous other studies serve to further affirm those messages, with the number of available studies now growing at a rapid pace.[23] The Millennium Ecosystem Assessment, initiated by the UN and released in 2005, offered a graphic representation of where we are and where we seem to be headed. One page of that report offers a pair of world maps, each with a bar graph superimposed on every continent. The upper map chronicles the number of major floods reported every decade from 1950 to 2000 on each continent; the lower map displays the number of major wildfires. Everywhere but in Oceania—which has faced such severe droughts that people now question whether major grain growing regions of Australia can still support any crops—the individual graphs rise steeply as the decades advance.[24] Over this time period, global temperatures only rose about one degree Fahrenheit (just over half a degree C); only the most optimistic of the IPCC's projected future scenarios limits further warming during this century to less than three additional degrees (1.5°C). Indeed the UN Environment Program projected in late 2009 that current policies would lead to a 3.5°C (6.3 degrees Fahrenheit) rise by 2100, and a study by the British Meteorological Office predicted an astounding 4°C (7°F) rise by 2060, resulting in worldwide droughts and heat waves, threatening water supplies for half the earth's population, and condemning half of all animal and plant species to extinction.[25] A 2009 symposium sponsored by the British Royal Society explored the consequences of 4 degrees warming, the level that will likely result from the continuation of business as usual.[26]

The biennial UN Human Development Report, issued in November of 2007, reported that one out of every 19 people in the so-called developing world was affected by a climate-related disaster between 2000 and 2004.[27] The figure for the wealthiest (OECD) countries was one out of every 1500 people. Yet the funds available thus far to various UN efforts to help the poorest countries adapt to climate changes ($26 million) is less than one week's worth of flood defense spending in the UK, and about what the city of Venice spends on its flood gates every 2-3 weeks. The report estimates that an additional $86 billion will be needed to sustain existing UN development assistance and poverty reduction programs in the face of all the various threats attributable to climate change.

A 2009 Oxfam study further confirmed that the effects of widespread climate disruptions are already with us. Oxfam found that of nearly 250 million people who are now affected by natural disasters every year, 98 percent of them are falling victim to climate-related events such as floods and droughts. They are predicting that this could quickly increase to over 375 million people per year.[28] Another study, published in the journal *Political Geography* by Rafael Reuveny of Indiana University, examined 38 cases over the past 70 years where populations were forced to migrate due to a combination of environmental (droughts, floods, storms, land degradation, pollution) and other factors.[29] Half of these cases led to violent conflict between the migrating populations and those in the receiving areas. It is clear, states Reuveny, that those who depend the most on the environment to sustain their livelihood, especially in regions where arable land and fresh water are scarce, are most likely to be forced to migrate when conditions are subjected to rapid and unplanned-for change.

Praful Bidwai, a former *Times of India* Senior Editor, drew attention in a recent article to the UN Conference on Trade and Development's 2010 *Least Developed Countries Report*, which stated that although those countries (LDCs)

> account for less than 1 per cent of the world's total GHG emissions, ... the frequency and intensity of extreme weather events in them are five times higher now (519 events in 2000-2010) than during the 1970s. In the last decade, about 40 per cent of all casualties related to natural disasters were found in LDCs, the poorest countries of the world.[30]

A 2007 report by the UK-based relief organization International Alert compared maps of the world's most politically unstable regions with those most susceptible to serious or extreme effects of climate change, and concluded that 46 countries, with a total population of 2.7 billion people, are firmly in both categories. The report, titled "A Climate of Conflict," states:

> "Hardest hit by climate change will be people living in poverty, in under-developed and unstable states, under poor governance. The effect of the physical consequences—such as more frequent extreme weather, melting glaciers, and shorter growing seasons—will add to the pressures under which those societies already live. The background of poverty and bad

governance means many of these communities both have a low capacity to adapt to climate change and face a high risk of violent conflict."[31]

International Alert's report profiled eight case studies of places in Africa and Asia where climate changes have already caused great stress on people's livelihoods and often exacerbated internal conflicts. The outlook is significantly improved, however, in places where political institutions are relatively stable and accountable to the population. This contrast allows for a somewhat hopeful conclusion, with the authors extolling "the synergies between climate adaptation policies and peace-building activities in achieving the shared goal of sustainable development and peace." One specific recommendation is to prioritize efforts to help people adapt to a changing climate, especially where subsistence-based economies contribute very little to global warming but are highly vulnerable to the consequences. Several international NGOs have already intervened, particularly in Africa, to document and disseminate changes in farming practices that have proven most useful in facilitating adaptation to a changing climate.

Since the Persian Gulf War of the early 1990s, activists have become increasingly aware of the devastating environmental consequences of warfare, and also of "peacetime" military activities. Oil consumption by the US military, for example, approaches 14 million gallons a day, according to peace studies scholar Michael Klare, more than is used daily in all of Sweden or Switzerland.[32] The US military is also responsible for thousands of toxic waste dumps on active and former bases around the world. An escalating spiral of warfare and environmental devastation threatens to spin entirely out of control if we are unable to achieve a different way of organizing the world's affairs. The world's militaries and elites are preparing themselves for the worst; those of us who seek peace and global justice need to come together as never before if those worst case scenarios are to be averted.

It is clear today that the past two centuries of capitalist development—and especially the unprecedented pace of resource consumption during the past 60 years—have created conditions that threaten everyone's future. "There could be no clearer demonstration than climate," says the UN's Human Development Report, "that economic wealth creation is not the same as human progress."[33] Those who have benefited the least from the unsustainable pace of economic growth and expansion since 1950 will face a future of suffering and dislocation unlike the world has ever seen, unless we can rapidly reverse the patterns of exploitation that many in the global North have simply come to take for granted.

How much warming can we tolerate?

A somewhat cautious note of triumph accompanied the pronouncement of the G8 heads of state in July of 2009 that the world was committing to holding the future average global temperature rise to below 2 degrees Celsius. The obstacle? "Developing Nations Rebuff G-8 on Curbing Pollutants," proclaimed the *New York Times* headline.[34] One had to read through most of the article to discover that the main objection of those pesky "developing nations" representatives was to affirming a long-range goal for reducing greenhouse gas emissions (a modest 50 percent reduction by 2050), without proportionate commitments from the major industrialized countries to nearer-term measures. They sought agreement on at least the 20 percent reductions by 2020 that were advocated by most European governments prior to Copenhagen, which could help facilitate progress toward the more distant goal. One astute European activist pointed out that the G8 outcome was "nothing but hot air," akin to pronouncing that there would be luxury resorts on Mars by 2050: with no intermediate goals nor tangible steps toward implementation, politicians can pledge to do anything at all 40+ years into the future. The 2 degree goal was eventually affirmed in the December 2009 Copenhagen Accord (see Chapter 2), and became the basis for most official discussions of the world's objectives for limiting global warming.

What, then, does 2 degrees of global warming mean? In April 2009, following a series of articles in the journal *Nature* that offered some important new revelations about the state of our climate projections, the climatologists who edit the indispensable scientific blog, RealClimate.org, wrote,

We feel compelled to note that even a 'moderate' warming of 2°C stands a strong chance of provoking drought and storm responses that could challenge civilized society, leading potentially to the conflict and suffering that go with failed states and mass migrations. Global warming of 2°C would leave the Earth warmer than it has been in millions of years, a disruption of climate conditions that have been stable for longer than the history of human agriculture. Given the drought that already afflicts Australia, the crumbling of the sea ice in the Arctic, and the increasing storm damage after only 0.8°C of warming so far, calling 2°C a danger limit seems to us pretty cavalier."[35]

Two degrees also turns out to be a rather daunting goal, in terms of the current world economy. At pre-recession rates of economic growth, with CO_2 emissions increasing 2 percent per year, we are virtually certain to exceed 2 degrees of warming by 2100, according to the European authors of the *Nature* 2-degrees study.[36] For a fifty-fifty chance of limiting warming to 2 degrees, developed countries would need to reduce their emissions by at least 80 percent over the next 40 years. There is a large uncertainty in that prediction, however, depending on the vagaries of the global carbon cycle and other hard-to-predict factors. The only reliable way to meet a 2 degree target is for cumulative world emissions to be kept below a rather austere target, equivalent to less than 400 billion tons of carbon between 2000 and 2050. Emissions since 2000 "have used up almost a third of that allowance already," according to a commentary by one of *Nature*'s US editors.[37]

Subsequent studies have proposed a remaining global carbon budget between 470 and 565 billion tons, a small fraction of the carbon contained in the world's known fossil fuel reserves.[38] And for all the trading and offsetting of CO_2 and other greenhouse gas emissions since the Kyoto Protocol was signed in 1997, only the recent economic downturn has led to substantial reductions in those emissions. Further, these projections often overlook emissions from agriculture, forestry, and a variety of related land use changes that are generally far more difficult to measure. The Kyoto Protocol, which required wealthy countries to reduce their emissions by 2012 to 6-8 percent below 1990 levels, "has produced no demonstrable reductions in emissions, or even in anticipated emissions growth," according to a widely cited report published in *Nature* in 2007.[39]

Meanwhile, a growing consensus of climate scientists and UN representatives from the global South insists that 2 degrees by no means a "safe" level of global warming. More recent research suggests that 2 degrees may be the point at which the likelihood of catastrophic, uncontrollable climate disruptions would reach about 50%, especially problematic since global emissions continue to rise.[40] Recent work by James Hansen and a team of global colleagues shows that global emissions would need to peak by around 2030 in order to return to a CO_2 concentration of 350 ppm within the next 2-300 years.[41] Considering the weather and sea-level effects of the warming the world has already experienced, the consensus among many global South delegates to the UN climate negotiations is that no more than 1-1.5 degrees of warming is tolerable. Given the long-term residence of CO_2 in the atmosphere, limiting warming to one degree would require an almost immediate cessation of fossil fuel combustion.

Global warming can represent a future of deprivation and scarcity for all but the world's wealthiest, or this global emergency can compel us to imagine a radically transformed society—both in the North and the South— where communities of people are newly empowered to create their own future. The crisis could potentially compel us to break free from a predatory global capitalism that fabulously enriches the top tenth of one percent, while leaving the rest of us scrambling after the crumbs. The reality is too urgent, and the outlook far too bleak, to settle for anything less than a radically new ecological social and political outlook. We need a movement that looks beyond the status-quo, actualizes the transformative potential of an ecological and justice-centered outlook, and illuminates the urgent necessity to create a dramatically different kind of world.

2

The UN Climate Negotiations and Beyond

The December 2009 United Nations climate summit in Copenhagen, Denmark was a watershed moment in the evolution of popular campaigns for climate action, and especially for climate justice. As those events recede into history, it is difficult to recapture the feeling of anticipation that engaged people from around the world during the preparations for Copenhagen. Many people involved in movements for climate action during that period held high hopes that the world's elites might finally begin to approach a meaningful long-term agreement. By the end, however, it appeared that the conference instead spurred a many years-long impasse, furthering a perhaps-inexorable slide toward an unstable and chaotic planetary climate regime—a world that our ancestors would barely recognize. Though some years have now passed since those landmark events, the particulars of the Copenhagen conference are important to recall in some detail. As we shall see, they have significantly shaped all subsequent developments in the world of climate diplomacy.

The Copenhagen conference was known officially as COP-15, the 15th Conference of the Parties to the UN's Framework Convention on Climate Change (UNFCCC). Even as close observers decried an increasing corporate influence over the preparations for COP-15, most participants held onto a shred of hope that something meaningful and significant would emerge from the negotiations. Seeing the urgency of the situation, prominent environmental groups, particularly Greenpeace, focused their strategy on urging US President Obama to personally participate in the Copenhagen summit. During earlier UN conferences the European Union had agreed to support faster reductions in carbon dioxide and other greenhouse gases. An end to US obstructionism, symbolized by the departure of President George W. Bush and the election of Barack Obama, might now clear the way toward a truly historic agreement. Instead, Obama's participation in Copenhagen demonstrated that US efforts to undermine the climate talks had evolved to a new, perhaps even more dangerous level, and the talks established a pattern of rhetorical flourish and substantive inaction that has continued for many years hence.

Yet on the eve of the Copenhagen summit officials appeared determined to spin the conference as a success, no matter what the outcome. Obama's announcement in early December 2009 that he would briefly appear in Copenhagen was a headline story, as was China's public commitment to reduce their economy's carbon intensity, effectively lowering the rate of *increase* in greenhouse gas emissions in their rapidly growing economy. Officials began to proclaim the advantages of a non-binding "political" or "operational" agreement as an incremental step toward reducing worldwide emissions. While some observers continued to anticipate a new binding global treaty to forestall catastrophic climate changes, the likelihood of such an agreement appeared to diminish with each passing week.

It wasn't supposed to be that way. For several years, environmentalists in North America, Europe, and around the world had anticipated that Copenhagen would be a decisive moment. Since the passage of the Kyoto Protocol in 1997, signatories to the Protocol, and to the more comprehensive UN climate convention, held major conferences nearly every year to further these documents' implementation. With the first so-called "commitment period" of Kyoto scheduled to end in 2012, the Copenhagen meeting was seen as the key to sustaining Kyoto's legacy of legally binding emissions reductions and perhaps preventing increasingly uncontrollable disruptions of the climate. This despite the highly ambiguous legacy of Kyoto, as we shall soon see.

For well over a year, environmentalists around the world were engaged in planning events, drafting reports, and coordinating action plans with the Copenhagen conference in mind. In October, the new 350.org network, initiated by Bill McKibben and several of his former students at Vermont's Middlebury College, staged a global day of action, reporting over 5200 documented activities in 181 countries.[1] These were aimed at dramatizing the need to reduce atmospheric carbon dioxide levels to below 350 parts per million and clearly timed to influence the COP. For much of the year, the timetable for Congressional action on US climate legislation was also partly focused toward the international stage. In July of 2009, eleven Greenpeace climbers scaled South Dakota's Mount Rushmore, famous for its larger-than-life stone images of four US presidents, to hang a gigantic banner featuring a portrait of Obama and the message, "America Honors Leaders, Not Politicians. Stop Global Warming."

By the mid-fall, however, public statements by both US and UN officials were pointedly aimed at lowering expectations. US climate negotiators remained evasive about what if any commitments they would bring to the table. The US Senate halted work on their highly flawed climate bill in mid-November, after a Republican boycott of hearings in Senator Barbara Boxer's Environment and Public Works Committee allowed only for the bill's pro-forma passage through the committee (see Chapter 4). In the midst of the preparatory meetings well in advance of Copenhagen, Martin Khor of the Malaysia-based Third World Network (now with the Geneva-based South Centre) and a decades-long participant in the UN process, wrote "not only is the climate in crisis, the climate talks are also in crisis."[2] Corporate representatives were hovering like vultures over UN climate meetings, seeking to define the terms of what they still hoped would be a rapidly expanding market in tradable carbon emissions allowances, and the World Bank gained control over funds to curtail deforestation, which is likely responsible for at least a quarter of current global warming. Even UNFCCC Executive Secretary Yvo de Boer began refocusing his public statements toward the "art of the possible."

One decisive rupture came during preparatory talks in Bangkok in mid-October, aimed at finalizing the framework for a Copenhagen agreement. For the first time, European Union representatives echoed the US refusal to make any future commitments to reduce greenhouse gas pollution under the framework established by the Kyoto Protocol. While previous UN climate meetings were aided by the Europeans' insistence on scientifically meaningful emission targets, this change—perhaps a perverse result of Obama's "improved" diplomacy—shifted the focus of the talks and raised the level of acrimony to new heights.[3] A month later, African delegates walked out of a follow-up meeting in Barcelona, and threatened to do the same in Copenhagen if rich countries refused to commit to meaningful reductions in greenhouse gas emissions. Finally, at a breakfast meeting during an Asia-Pacific economic summit in Singapore in mid-November, Obama and Danish Prime Minister Rasmussen announced that a legally binding climate treaty was not forthcoming, and would take at least another year to negotiate.

Beyond Kyoto?

Activists wondered how and why the world had gotten to this point of apparent impasse. Part of the problem stemmed from the flaws inherent in the Kyoto Protocol, but much of the blame appeared to rest with US policymakers, who appeared to be working behind the scenes to undermine Copenhagen for quite some time, as we will see. To complicate things further, negotiators often voiced conflicting interpretations of what the Kyoto Protocol meant and to what degree it should help define the terms of future agreements.

In important ways, the 1997 Kyoto Protocol represented a crucial breakthrough in the ongoing UNFCCC process. For the first time, countries agreed to a schedule of binding targets for reducing emissions of greenhouse gases and a prescribed means for working toward those targets. The primary responsibility for emissions reductions fell on the richest countries, with the rest of the world accepting "common but differentiated responsibilities" (in the language of the 1992 climate convention) to mitigate a potential climate crisis. The devil, as always, was in the details, and those details were in many ways a product of then-Vice President Al Gore's interventions in Kyoto.

Gore arrived in Kyoto toward the end of the conference, at a point when the US refusal to sign on to mandatory emissions cuts had threatened to derail the proceedings. Gore was widely credited with saving the day; specifically he offered that the US would sign on to a Kyoto Protocol under two conditions. First, mandated reductions in emissions would be limited to roughly half of what was originally proposed, and second, emissions cuts would be implemented through the market-based trading of "rights to pollute" among various companies and between countries. This was the first use of carbon trading (only later described as "cap-and-trade"—see Chapter 4) as a primary instrument of international policy. While the US never ratified the Kyoto Protocol, the rest of the world has had to live with the consequences, namely a cumbersome but corporate-friendly carbon trading system that has failed to bring needed pollution reductions, along with an even more unwieldy scheme allowing companies to offset their emissions by investing in nominally low-carbon projects in the global South.

A decade later, the process was further complicated by the so-called Bali Action Plan that emerged from the 2007 UN climate summit on the island of Bali in Indonesia. This plan allowed for the negotiations toward Copenhagen to proceed on two tracks, one continuing the process laid out in the Kyoto Protocol, and the other essentially going back to the drawing board of the original 1992 climate convention. While Kyoto remained a legally binding treaty, developing nations' representatives proved justified in their fears that this second track would be used to create a superseding agreement and thus overturn the modest gains that poor countries achieved in Kyoto. At the center of the debates in Copenhagen and beyond was the US and its allies' effort to overturn Kyoto's non-distinction between rapidly developing nations such as China and the world's poorest countries; that circumstance brought China to the fore as a key advocate for those seeking to retain the Kyoto framework. The US repeatedly blamed China and India for their rapidly rising CO_2 levels, as well as for keeping a new international climate agreement from moving forward entirely on the North's terms. The G77 group of developing countries and the Alliance of Small Island States—who have the most to lose if there is no international agreement and sea levels continue to rise—all lined up in support of retaining Kyoto and holding the richest nations responsible for their historic contribution to destabilizing the climate.

Technology transfer funds were another key sticking point in the pre-Copenhagen talks. If poorer countries are to eventually bring their emissions down and simultaneously lift people out of poverty, Northern countries will need to fulfill their Kyoto commitments to speed the deployment of renewable energy technologies in the South. Meanwhile, indigenous peoples' representatives such as Anastasia Pinto of CORE, based in India's Eastern Himalayas, viewed such "sustainable development" arguments as mainly benefiting elites in the South, who want to continue getting richer at the expense of both poor people and the environment. During a fall 2009 US tour, Pinto described India's growing economic divide as the real key to their government's refusal to limit India's rising contribution to the climate crisis. Former *Times of India* Senior Editor Praful Bidwai similarly points a finger at India's "small but exceedingly powerful consumerist elite..., which has a high stake in raising its emissions and believes it has the 'right' to 'get even' with the North, no matter what happens to the climate."[4] This complex interplay of responsibilities and interests, linked to the historical legacy of colonialism and the contentious politics of "development," contributed in many ways to Copenhagen's eventual impasse.

Lim Li Lin of the Third World Network summed up one key aspect of the deadlock over Kyoto in a pre-conference briefing paper, stating, "The international compliance regime under the Kyoto Protocol ... faces an uncertain future. While it can always be further improved, the risk is now the possibility of no longer having a system of international compliance."[5] Perhaps the strongest argument in favor of Kyoto was that it could prove far more costly to the environment in the long run to try to develop a new climate treaty from scratch, especially if the worst features of Kyoto—namely the cap-and-trade system—would be retained in either case.

Revealing the US Strategy

While attempts to preserve aspects of the Kyoto Protocol were burdened by all the complexities of North-South politics, the continued resistance of the US government to internationally binding limits on global warming pollution raised many fundamental questions. Is there any defensible alternative to a mutually agreed-upon effort to reduce worldwide greenhouse gas emissions? Just what was the US bringing to the table in Copenhagen beside a vague pledge to reduce emissions by 2020 to a level that still fell far short of many countries' 2012 commitments under Kyoto?[6]

An article in the September/October 2009 issue of the journal *Foreign Affairs* offered some important clues as to what would transpire in Copenhagen and beyond. *Foreign Affairs* is the official organ of the Council on Foreign Relations (CFR), which has long been seen as both a weathervane and an active arbiter of elite opinion in the US, and lists most recent US presidents and numerous other senior government officials among its members. In his article titled "Copenhagen's Inconvenient Truth," CFR Senior Fellow Michael Levi outlined the US government's apparently long-standing strategy for Copenhagen.[7]

"The odds of signing a comprehensive treaty in December are vanishingly small," Levi would need to have written early in the summer, in preparation for the journal's early September publication. Instead, he urged that those concerned about the climate problem needed to "rethink their strategy and expectations" for Copenhagen. Levi's alternative proposal was to essentially replace international emissions standards with a patchwork of voluntary, country-specific policies with the modest, and fundamentally inadequate, goal of reducing world emissions of carbon dioxide by half, "ideally from 1990 levels, by 2050." Under Levi's scenario, China would step up investments in renewable energy and "ultra-efficient conventional coal power," India would become a pioneer in smart grid technology, and countries with emissions mainly from deforestation (especially Indonesia and Brazil) would be offered incentives to protect their forests and raise agricultural productivity. The main US contribution would be to push for a detailed agreement on "measurement, reporting and verification," one area where US surveillance technology would clearly hold an advantage.

Levi's article pointedly blamed developing countries for the world's inability to agree on meaningful emission caps. He argued that the Chinese and others invariably insist on lower-than-feasible caps, lack the capacity to accurately monitor their emissions, and would simply ignore any limits that they proved unable to meet. Unfortunately, this is precisely how Northern countries have behaved since Kyoto; indeed Levi cited Canada as a key example of a country that repeatedly exceeded its Kyoto limits, and faced no penalty for doing so. For these reasons, according to Levi, efforts to develop binding caps for developing countries are simply "a waste of time."

A key challenge for the US in Copenhagen, according to Levi, was to avoid "excessive blame" if the conference were to be seen as a failure. Rather than expecting a comprehensive agreement to come out of Copenhagen, he argued, the conference should instead be seen as analogous to the beginning of a round of arms control or world trade talks, processes which invariably take many years to complete. "This 'Copenhagen Round,'" he argues, mirroring the typical World Trade Organization (WTO) language, "would be much more like an extended trade negotiation than like a typical environmental treaty process." Overlooking the fact that a substantive, though flawed, agreement was actually signed in Kyoto, he emphasized that it took several more years of negotiations before that treaty could be implemented.

The implications of such a Copenhagen non-agreement were clearly going to be severe. Climate scientists emphasized that time is rapidly running out to prevent irreversible tipping points in the destabilization of the earth's climate. Trends in CO_2 emissions were already exceeding the worst-case "business-as-usual" scenarios of the Intergovernmental Panel on Climate Change's 2007 report, and researchers were beginning to predict temperature rises of 4 degrees or more (7 degrees Fahrenheit) in various regions of the world, well before the end of this century.[8] That would mean a permanent loss of Arctic ice, accellerating spells of flooding and droughts, threats to half the earth's fresh water supplies, and the collapse of countless important ecosystems as well as key agricultural zones.

Meanwhile, climate justice activists in Europe, in indigenous and small farming communities worldwide, as well as in North America, challenged the inequities underlying current climate policies and demanded real solutions. They highlighted the voices of the communities most affected by the climate changes that are already underway, and challenged corporate-friendly false solutions, from carbon trading and offsets, to the myths of "clean coal," nuclear power, and the onslaught of industrial-scale agrofuel plantations. Simultaneously, they challenged the growing dominance of corporate interests in the UN process itself, a phenomenon that led one participant in the 2007 UN climate conference in Bali to describe it as "a giant shopping extravaganza, marketing the earth, the sky and the rights of the poor."[9]

Climate justice activists in North America held a continent-wide day of action on Monday, November 30th, the tenth anniversary of the mass demonstrations that helped shut down the World Trade Organization in Seattle. Hundreds of people marched and rallied and dozens were arrested at locations from San Francisco's Bank of America headquarters to the Chicago Climate Exchange, then home of the largest voluntary carbon market. South Carolina activists blocked the shipment of a generator for a new coal plant, Canadians sat in at the office of their Finance Minister—a key proponent of the massively destructive scheme to extract oil from the tar sands of central Alberta—and New Yorkers marched from a local Bank of America to the offices of the Natural Resources Defense Council, a leading environmental advocate for carbon trading.[10]

The following weekend, thousands marched in Geneva during the World Trade Organization's first ministerial conference in four years. The momentum was building for massive actions on the streets of Copenhagen, where many activists would demand "System Change, Not Climate

Change." They called for fossil fuels to be kept in the ground, indigenous and forest peoples' rights to be respected, and reparations for ecological and climate debts to be paid by the richest countries to those who are most affected by resource extraction and climate-related disasters. For some advocates, Copenhagen represented capitalism's last possible attempt to come to terms with the climate crisis. With African delegates threatening another walkout, and the US pushing for an agreement in name only, the analogy raised by international activists between the Copenhagen climate conference and the November 1999 WTO meeting in Seattle looked to be more appropriate than most environmentalists ever imagined.

Coercive Diplomacy

For the emerging international climate justice movement, Copenhagen was indeed something of a Seattle moment, with some 100,000 people in the streets on the Saturday between the two weeks of talks. It was a unique opportunity for activists and NGO representatives from around the world to gather, forge personal ties, and begin raising the global profile of a comprehensive climate justice agenda. Independent journalists (in the US, most notably Amy Goodman's *Democracy Now* team) helped amplify the voices best able to explain that climate disruptions are no longer an abstract scientific issue, and are already impacting the lives of those least able to cope. Even the mainstream US press featured some notable stories of people around the world who are struggling with the effects of climate chaos. More than ever before, the street actions in Copenhagen dramatized the view that the only meaningful solution to the climate crisis is to "leave the oil in the soil, the coal in the hole, and the tar sands in the land," expanding upon a slogan initially raised by campaigners against oil drilling in Ecuador's endangered Yasuní National Park.

Copenhagen was also a pivotal moment for the ALBA (Bolivarian Alliance) countries of Latin America—most notably Bolivia, Nicaragua, and Venezuela—which continued to the very end of the conference to stand up to threats from the US and other powerful countries, and refused to buckle under last-minute pressure to approve the shallow and destructive "Copenhagen Accord." In the end, the assembled delegates could only agree to "take note" of the five-page Accord. The European Union, on the other hand, which had once stood for a strong worldwide agreement on greenhouse gas emissions, now fell in line with the disruptive strategies of the US. Even though the final document was not formally accepted until the following year, Copenhagen represented a triumph of the US agenda to replace the promise of a comprehensive global climate agreement with a patchwork of informal, individual country commitments.

Ultimately, the Copenhagen Accord served to establish the notion of voluntary national pledges as a new global norm for implementing climate policy. Nothing was binding on governments or corporations, and pledges were only to be "assessed" informally after five years. The last two pages of the Accord actually consisted of a pair of empty charts where countries were to simply fill in their voluntary emissions targets and other proposed mitigation actions by the end of January 2010. Fifty-five countries ultimately met that deadline, essentially putting in writing their negotiating positions prior to the Copenhagen meeting. Another twenty countries submitted their pledges in the months that followed. Hillary Clinton, then the US Secretary of State, had promised global South countries that acceded to the Copenhagen Accord that the US would raise $100 billion a year in funds to assist with climate stabilizing measures, a promise that all but evaporated during subsequent years' negotiations.

Further, the document was hammered out in a back room, WTO-style. It hedged all the important issues, and appended loopholes and contradictions to every substantive point that it pretended to address. While discussions would continue for at least five more years under the two separate negotiating tracks established in Bali, the Accord provided a justification for leading countries in the process to continue subverting and undermining those discussions in order to continue business as usual.

As some have pointed out, it could have been worse. This non-agreement may have been better than a coercive agreement that would have entrenched insufficient pollution reduction targets and facilitated the further expansion of highly manipulated global carbon markets. But the putative loss of a nominally accountable UN process may have been the worst outcome of all. The US, of course, has always tried to undermine the United Nations when it is unable to overtly control it, but replacing the processes established under the 1992 UN climate convention with a cash-for-compliance, anything-goes circus that more closely mirrors the World Trade Organization's secretive mechanisms did not bode well for the future.

Representatives of Friends of the Earth correctly described the Copenhagen Accord as a "sham agreement," British columnist George Monbiot called it an exercise in "saving face," and former neoliberal "shock doctor"-turned-environmental policy guru Jeffrey Sachs termed it a farce.[11] Long-time UN observer Martin Khor has pointed out that for the assembled countries to "take note" of the document meant that not only was it not formally adopted, but it was not even "welcomed," a common UN practice.[12]

The Accord also heightened the global divide between rich and poor, with countries experiencing the severest droughts, floods, and heatwaves facing increasingly desperate fates as the full effects of climate disruptions continue to unfold. Not to mention the small island nations that face annihilation as melting ice sheets and thermal expansion bring rising seas, along with infiltrations of seawater into their scarce fresh water supplies. Especially disturbing in Copenhagen was the equivocal role of the rapidly developing "BASIC" countries (Brazil, South Africa, India and China), whose governments claim to speak for the poor when it is convenient—whether in their own countries or elsewhere around the world—but mainly seek to protect the expanding riches of their own well-entrenched elites, who are all to willing to do the bidding of transnational corporate interests. While the mainstream media in the North preferred to blame China for the lack of a more comprehensive agreement in Copenhagen, a convergence of Chinese and US elite economic interests was clearly manifest in the Copenhagen Accord's transparent lack of substance.

Beyond Copenhagen

In April of 2010, researchers from Germany's most prestigious climate research centers published a paper in *Nature* that summarized various countries' emission reduction commitments under the Copenhagen Accord and assessed their likely consequences for the global climate.[13] Most countries, they found, were projecting greenhouse gas levels in 2020 roughly comparable to a business-as-usual scenario, thoroughly lacking in substantial measures to curtail global warming pollution. Only Japan and Norway, among the developed countries, had pledged to accomplish significantly more than that. Many countries' pledges, they observed, would be fulfilled using surplus emission allowances that they held in reserve due to the systematic over-allocation of allowances condoned by the Kyoto Protocol (see Chapter 4). Even a best-case scenario, based on the upper limit of various countries' mitigation commitments, came in far short of holding the likely rise in average-global temperature within the range of 2 degrees Celsius that was "recognized" as scientifically defensible in the Accord's text. The German researchers' more pessimistic scenario projected developed countries' emissions in 2020 as equivalent to a 6.5 percent *increase* in greenhouse gases from the 1990 baseline, corresponding to an eventual global average temperature increase of at least 5 degrees (9°Fahrenheit). In unusually descriptive language for the traditionally rather staid pages of *Nature*, the German group decried the lack of accepted short-term emission-reduction goals as equivalent to "racing towards a cliff and hoping to stop just before it."[14]

One of the signature moments in Copenhagen was Bolivian president Evo Morales' invitation to those assembled to participate in a different kind of climate summit in the Bolivian city of Cochabamba the following April. The 2010 "World People's Conference on Climate Change and the Rights of Mother Earth" turned out to be a rather unique coming together of public officials from a few countries with some 30,000 representatives of civil society, indigenous peoples, and social movements from around the world. They collectively drafted a comprehensive set of principles, rooted in indigenous views of harmony, complementarity and anti-colonialism, proposed a Universal Declaration on the Rights of Mother Earth, and called for an International Climate and Environmental Justice Tribunal to judge and penalize activities that promote climate change and contaminate the earth.[15]

The Cochabamba "People's Agreement," which was assembled from the products of 17 distinct working groups at the conference, began by declaring that, "Today, our Mother Earth ["Pachamama" in the Andean indigenous cosmology] is wounded and the future of humanity is in danger." The agreement condemned carbon markets, as well as the commodification of forests for carbon offsets, and also called to protect the rights of climate migrants. It represented a rather refreshing step beyond the diplomatic gridlock of Copenhagen, even though the agreement fell short of endorsing the full climate justice agenda, especially the demand to keep fossil fuels in the ground. The contents of the Cochabamba agreement were presented as proposals to the 2010 and 2011 UN climate conferences, but repeatedly failed to reach the floor of the official plenaries.

Since Copenhagen, progress toward a meaningful climate agreement has continued to be stifled by big-power politics and diplomatic gridlock. Annual conferences under the auspices of the UNFCCC have happened in Mexico, South Africa, Qatar, and Poland, with conferences planned as of this writing in Lima, Peru toward the end of 2014 and Paris in 2015. Participants and civil society observers at recent COPs have witnessed numerous disturbing developments, including:

- Increasing polarization between representatives from the North and South, particularly in response to US efforts to dilute the long-standing focus on "common but differentiated responsibilities" for climate mitigation and remove the more explicit language on climate equity that has long been intrinsic to the UNFCCC process;[16]
- Unilateral withdrawal from the Kyoto Protocol on the part of most leading countries outside of Western Europe that were subject to its binding emissions limits, including Japan, Australia, Canada, Russia, and New Zealand;
- A 2011 agreement that a new climate treaty would not come into effect until 2020, with the terms slated to be finalized in Paris in 2015; its implementation will likely rely on the system of national mitigation pledges (now termed "contributions," with undefined legal standing) that the US has insisted upon since Copenhagen, and dissenting voices from the ALBA countries and elsewhere have been largely ignored;
- Small concessions to G77 countries along the way, mostly aimed at keeping them engaged in the process. These included the creation of a new structure in 2013 for addressing ongoing

losses and damages from climate disruptions, but the means for
funding this remain vague.

The 2011 "Durban Platform," with its deferral of new climate
mitigation measures until 2020 at the earliest, heightened
a lingering crisis of confidence in the entire process. That
delay could spell a "death sentence for Africa, small island
states, and the poor and vulnerable worldwide," in the
words of Friends of the Earth International chair Nnimmo
Bassey, and increasing "climate racism, ecocide, and
genocide," according to Tom Goldtooth of the Indigenous
Environmental Network.[17] Additionally, the pledge of $100
billion a year in climate-related financing for developing
countries, which was crucial to convincing many countries to
let the process to move forward in Copenhagen, has proved
increasingly uncertain. Each successive annual conference
has come close to adjourning without any new substantive
agreements, despite dramatically lowered expectations and
an increasingly coercive decision-making process. Global
South delegates walked out of the 2013 COP in Warsaw,
Poland *en masse* to protest their continuing marginalization;
meanwhile the Polish government added insult to injury that
year by sponsoring a conference celebrating the country's
coal industry that coincided with the COP.

A revealing 2013 speech by lead US climate negotiator
Todd Stern brought an especially alarming glimpse at
where the entire process may be headed. Stern continued
the pattern of blaming poorer countries for resisting an
"agreement applicable to all parties," and touted the emphasis
on "self-determined mitigation commitments" instead of

mandatory obligations to reduce emissions. He dismissed the "loss and damage" negotiations that would dominate many discussions in Warsaw as merely an "ideological narrative of fault and blame," and insisted that no additional public funds for international climate aid would be available beyond the meager \$2.5 billion that the US has committed annually since 2010. Further, he thoroughly rejected the long-standing principle of responsibility for historical CO_2 emissions, insisting, with unsurpassed arrogance, that, "It is unwarranted to assign blame to developed countries for emissions before the point at which people realized that those emissions caused harm to the climate system."[18] Ethics aside, Stern would have us all forget that at least half of all cumulative emissions have occurred since 1980, and a much larger share since the first observations of rising atmospheric CO_2 levels in the late 1950s.

So for now the struggle returns to the national and local levels, where people may be best able to create examples of just and effective ways to address the climate crisis. There is no shortage of positive, forward-looking approaches to reducing excess consumption and furthering the development of alternative energy sources, especially ones that can be democratically controlled by communities and not corporations. But the power of positive examples is far from sufficient to address the crucial problem of time.

A few years ago, climate experts shocked the world by saying we had less than ten years to reverse course and take immediate steps to prevent irreversible tipping points in the global climate system. The troubled outcome of the UN process, and continued diplomatic stonewalling in the lead-up to future worldwide agreements, make it difficult to feel confident that it isn't too late. Now, any meaningful turnaround will require the evolution of an increasingly unified and effective international climate justice movement. In the next chapter, we will turn to the question of how such a movement has begun to take shape.

3

Toward a Movement for Climate Justice

On the Indonesian island of Bali in late 2007, events surrounding the annual UN climate conference had a strikingly different character than had been seen before. Previous gatherings had brought NGO and civil society representatives from various countries to politely participate in the proceedings and sometimes to demonstrate outside. But the diversity of peoples and issues in Bali was by all accounts a unique site to behold. Colorful costumes and distinctive headgear represented the unique ethnic diversity of Indonesia's islands, as well as a wide scope of people's movements from across south Asia and beyond.

The diversity of climate-related issues and public demands raised by the demonstrators was equally impressive. Two years earlier, the leading symbol at protests outside the 2005 climate talks in Montreal was the ubiquitous polar bear. In

Bali, representatives of land-based peoples' movements demanded agrarian reform, an end to conversions of tropical forest into biofuel plantations, and the protection of peatlands. Others called for payment of the global North's outstanding ecological debts and for an end to the biotechnology industry's commodification of life.[1] A new global network calling itself Climate Justice Now raised a challenging new set of demands both inside and outside the official proceedings.

In the fall of 2008, U.S. organizations actively working for climate justice in the US and internationally, including the Global Justice Ecology Project, Rising Tide North America, and the Indigenous Environmental Network, launched a national Mobilization for Climate Justice. The Mobilization was founded to link the climate struggle in the US to the growing international climate justice movement, with an eye toward the 2009 Copenhagen climate summit and beyond. Its objective was to provide a justice-based framework for organizing around climate change that sought leadership from communities in the US that are most impacted by climate change and the fossil fuel industry. The MCJ's open letter to potential allies called for "a radical change in direction to put climate justice, ecological integrity and people's rights at the center of international climate negotiations."[2] Another new network, Climate SOS emerged soon afterward to expose the myths of the carbon market as promoted in domestic US legislation.

The following year, European activists engaged in planning events around the climate conference in Copenhagen began to see that the summit would likely fall far short of preventing further climate disruptions, and pledged to take action against the root causes of climate change. Activists from more than 20 countries, including several from the global South, gathered that summer as part of a network called Climate Justice Action, and agreed on an ambitious agenda to challenge the increasingly business-dominated deal-making at the UN level.

"We cannot trust the market with our future, nor put our faith in unsafe, unproven and unsustainable technologies," their declaration read. "Contrary to those who put their faith in 'green capitalism,' we know that it is impossible to have infinite growth on a finite planet."[3] The statement called for leaving fossil fuels in the ground, popular and community control over production, reducing the North's overconsumption, respecting indigenous and forest peoples' rights and reparations for the ecological and climate debts owed by the richest countries to those most affected by resource extraction and climate-related disasters.

Today, representatives of communities disproportionately affected by global inaction on climate gather annually at the UN climate meetings, and aim to coordinate their actions throughout the year around a broad scope of local and regional grievances as well. People from communities disproportionately affected by climate disruptions— especially indigenous peoples, women, peasant farmers, US racial justice activists and many others—gather in host cities to bring their demands to the world. Calls for climate justice, and for "System Change, Not Climate Change," have become familiar highlights of these proceedings.

This emerging climate justice movement embodies the core understanding that those least responsible for emissions of carbon dioxide and other greenhouse gases that disrupt the climate have already been affected the most by accelerating climate-related disasters around the world. Any remotely adequate response to global climate changes needs to address and directly challenge this profound discrepancy and prioritize the voices of the most affected communities. Many of the same communities are simultaneously impacted by the emerging false solutions to climate change, including carbon trading and offsets, the destruction of forests to create agrofuel plantations, mega-scale hydroelectric developments, and nuclear power (see Chapter 4). False corporate "solutions" to global warming are expanding commodification and privatization of land, waterways, and the atmosphere itself, largely at the expense of those communities.

Origins of Climate Justice

The first published reference to the concept of climate justice appeared in a 1999 report titled *Greenhouse Gangsters vs. Climate Justice* by the San Francisco-based Corporate Watch group.[4] The report was mainly an examination of the petroleum industry and its disproportionate political influence, but it also made an initial attempt to define a multifaceted approach to climate justice, including:

- Addressing the root causes of global warming and holding corporations accountable;
- Opposing the destructive impacts of oil development, and supporting impacted communities, including those most affected by the increasing incidence of weather-related disasters;

- Looking to environmental justice communities (see below) and organized labor for strategies to support a just transition away from fossil fuels;
- Challenging corporate-led globalization and the disproportionate influence of international financial institutions such as the World Bank and World Trade Organization.

The report's conclusions were highlighted at a 1999 rally at Chevron Oil's headquarters in San Francisco, as well as at international conferences held in the Netherlands in 2000 and on the Indonesian island of Bali in 2002.

The Corpwatch authors were active supporters of the US movement for environmental justice, which began in earnest in the 1980s and had become a focus for inner city, indigenous, and poor rural communities confronting their disproportionate exposure to a wide variety of environmental hazards. The movement was galvanized by several successful local campaigns, as well as a landmark, church-sponsored report, *Toxic Wastes and Race*, which revealed that the racial composition of communities is the single largest factor in the siting of hazardous waste facilities in the US. The report documented that 3 out of 5 African-Americans nationwide live in close proximity to abandoned toxic sites.[5]

News of the *Toxic Wastes and Race* report helped unite a variety of groups that had been challenging this reality on the local level for many years, and helped empower African American, Native American and Latino activists to demand a greater voice within the largely Euro-American-dominated environmental movement.[6] In 1991, a National

People of Color Environmental Leadership Summit issued a comprehensive public statement against environmental racism and for environmental justice.[7] By the mid-1990s, Tom Goldtooth of the Indigenous Environmental Network (IEN) and others were articulating the need to bring the deepening climate crisis into the environmental justice framework, understanding that people of color would be as disproportionately impacted by climate disruptions as by chemical toxins. The movement's second Leadership Summit in 2002 issued a document titled "10 Principles for Just Climate Change Policies in the US."[8]

Also throughout the 1990s, international NGOs such as the World Rainforest Movement, Friends of the Earth International and the Third World Network drew public attention to local struggles of indigenous and other land-based peoples in the global South against the rising levels of resource extraction that accompanied neoliberal economic policies. They joined with Corpwatch, IEN and others in Bali in 2002 to develop the Bali Principles of Climate Justice, a comprehensive, 27-point program aimed to "begin to build an international movement of all peoples for Climate Justice."[9] Campaigns to highlight indigenous land struggles helped shape the international movement against corporate-driven globalization in the late 1990s and early 2000s, and became a central focus for numerous organizations engaged in international climate justice organizing today, including IEN, the Global Forest Coalition, the Global Justice Ecology Project, and many others.[10]

During the lead-up to the final ratification of the Kyoto Protocol in 2005, policymakers in the EU and other countries increasingly adopted market-based "cap-and-trade" measures to nominally reduce greenhouse pollution (see Chapter 4). Market skeptics, concerned about the injustices inherent in this approach, convened a meeting in Durban, South Africa in the fall of 2004 that included representatives of social movements and indigenous peoples' organizations based in Brazil, India, Samoa, the US, and UK, as well as South Africa. That gathering drafted the Durban Declaration on Carbon Trading, which eventually gained over 300 endorsements worldwide.[11]

When the U.N.'s annual climate conference was held in Bali in 2007, the Durban Group for Climate Justice and allies from around the world gathered in significant numbers. Representatives of communities disproportionately affected by global inaction on climate presented a strong and unified showing both inside and outside the official proceedings and, as we have seen, a more formal worldwide network emerged under the slogan, "Climate Justice Now!" At a series of side events, press conferences and protests throughout the Bali conference, representatives of affected communities, indigenous peoples, women, peasant farmers, and their allies articulated their demands for:

- reduced consumption in the global North;
- huge financial transfers from North to South based on historical responsibility and ecological debt, paid for by redirecting military budgets, innovative taxes and debt cancellation;
- leaving fossil fuels in the ground and investing in energy-efficiency and community-led renewable energy;
- rights based resource conservation that enforces Indigenous

77

> land rights and promotes peoples' sovereignty over energy, forests, land and water; and

- sustainable family farming and food sovereignty.[12]

A more detailed statement of principles for Climate Justice Now (CJN), developed the following year, begins in part:

> From the perspective of climate justice, it is imperative that responsibility for reducing emissions and financing systemic transformation is taken by those who have benefited most from the past 250 years of economic development. Furthermore, any solutions to climate change must protect the most vulnerable, compensate those who are displaced, guarantee individual and collective rights, and respect peoples' right to participate in decisions that impact on their lives.[13]

By 2010, the CJN network included some 750 international organizations, including numerous grassroots groups throughout the global South, and had become a clearinghouse for information and the continuing involvement of many groups seeking to further these goals.[14] At several UN climate conferences, the network offered an inclusive meeting place for critical perspectives on the unfolding international climate negotiations.

In recent years, climate justice has come to embody three distinct but complementary currents from various parts of the world. In the global South, demands for climate justice unite an impressive diversity of indigenous and other land-based people's movements. They include rainforest dwellers opposing new mega-dams and palm oil plantations, African communities resisting land appropriations for industrial agriculture and agrofuel production, Pacific Islanders facing the loss of their homes due to rising seas, and peasant farmers fighting for food sovereignty and basic land rights. A statement to the 2009 Copenhagen climate conference from the worldwide confederation of peasant movements, La Vía Campesina, stated in part:

> Climate change is already seriously impacting us. It brings floods, droughts and the outbreak of pests that are all causing harvest failures. I must point out that these harvest failures are something that the farmers did not create. Instead, it is the polluters who caused the emissions who destroy the natural cycles… [W]e will not pay for their mistakes.[15]

In the US, environmental justice activists continue to be the leading voices for climate justice—mainly representatives from African American, Latino and Native American communities that have been resisting daily exposure to chemical toxins and other environmental hazards for 30 years. A 2008 report from the Oakland, California-based Environmental Justice and Climate Change Initiative pointed out that African Americans may be at the greatest risk, both from disruptive climate changes and from exposure to the negative effects of various false solutions. The six US states with the highest African American populations are all in the Atlantic hurricane zone, and African Americans also have the highest historic rates of heat death.[16] They have the highest asthma rates and spend the highest percentage of their income on energy. A 2009 study by several public health professionals confirmed the disproportionate consequences of heat-related illness for communities of color in the US, exacerbated by people's lack of access to transportation and other essential needs.[17] These findings, and the experiences of frontline communities across the US—from the melting Alaskan tundra to the Louisiana coast—highlight the urgency of a more astute and holistic climate justice movement.

An important two day conference in New York City in early 2009, organized by West Harlem Environmental Action (WEACT), brought together racial justice activists, community and youth organizers, indigenous representatives and farmworker advocates with students, environmental lawyers, scientists, public health advocates and government officials to discuss the relevance of the climate justice framework for communities of color and their allies across the US.[18] Many speakers described the emerging climate justice movement as a continuation of the US civil rights legacy, and of their communities' continuing "quest for fairness, equity and justice," as described by the pioneering environmental justice researcher and author, Robert Bullard."[19] Others explained how, in recent years, the environmental justice movement has broadened its scope to areas of food justice, housing justice, and transportation justice, as well as opposition to the commodification of the atmosphere through global carbon markets. A physician from Los Angeles described carbon trading as yet another means of "redistributing wealth from the poor to the wealthy," and José Bravo of the Just Transition Alliance suggested that "when we put a price on every square inch of air, there are some of us who won't be able to afford to breathe."

In much of Europe, climate justice emerged as a further evolution of the global justice and anticapitalist movements that arose in opposition to the World Trade Organization (WTO) and annual G8 economic summits during the late 1990s and early 2000s. A March 2010 discussion paper from the European Climate Justice Action network (CJA) explained that "Climate Justice means linking all struggles together that reject neoliberal markets and working towards a world that puts autonomous decision making power in the hands of communities." The paper concluded: "Fundamentally, we believe that we cannot prevent further global warming without addressing the way our societies are organized—the fight for climate justice and the fight for social justice are one and the same."[20] While Climate Justice Action proved to be relatively short-lived, this approach has been sustained by ongoing networks such as Rising Tide as well as the UK Climate Camp movement, which organized high profile actions between 2006 and 2010 at major power plant sites, Heathrow Airport, London's financial district, and the Edinburgh headquarters of the Royal Bank of Scotland.[21]

The role of Rising Tide is especially noteworthy as an international voice for direct action to challenge climate polluters, as well as a long-range systemic critique of the underlying causes of climate disruptions. Formed in the lead-up to the November 2000 UN climate conference in the Hague, Netherlands, Rising Tide recently listed six regional affiliates— North America (US and Canada), UK, Mexico, Ecuador, Australia and Finland—as well as organizing collectives in several US states and regions. Made up mostly of youthful activists with roots in decentralist and anti-authoritarian political traditions, Rising Tide has supported numerous direct action campaigns against both the fossil fuel industry and a variety of corporate-driven false solutions to the climate crisis. Rising Tide has organized and trained participants for many high-profile direct actions, especially in the US, UK, and Australia, and is also noted for its critical educational efforts.[22]

Climate Justice and the Future

In the aftermath of Copenhagen's diplomatic meltdown, some in Europe questioned whether a unified climate justice movement could survive. The Copenhagen effort, according to CJA activists Nicola Bullard and Tadzio Müller,

> failed to establish an anti-capitalist CJ-discourse that was visible and understandable beyond the subcultures of activists and policy-wonks, and thus failed to provide a visible alternative to despair; failed to establish a new "pole of attraction" that would substantially reconfigure the political field around climate change; and failed to do anything to significantly advance the fight for climate justice. In some sense, the *global* CJM [Climate Justice Movement; emphasis in original] remained something more of a potential than a reality.[23]

In the US as well, events organized during the lead-up to Copenhagen also represented a peak in public visibility for climate justice for some years hence. Along with the regional actions timed to coincide with the tenth anniversary of the WTO shutdown in Seattle (see Chapter 2), the Mobilization for Climate Justice-West (MCJ-West) in the San Francisco

Bay Area organized seven high-profile demonstrations during the five months prior to Copenhagen, including several in solidarity with a decades-long effort by activists in the largely African-American city of Richmond, California to confront the hazards of a major Chevron oil refinery.

However MCJ-West found it internally unsustainable to maintain that level of public visibility into 2010 and beyond, and a principled effort to restructure the group to better reflect the priorities of local community-based organizations proved insufficient to keep the group afloat. The fledgling national Mobilization also ceased to operate following a similar internal discussion. While participants generally agreed that frontline environmental justice communities are inherently in the forefront of climate justice organizing, community-based organizations struggling with the daily impacts of political and economic marginalization did not appear to have the capacity, nor perhaps the inclination, to sustain a unified national climate justice coalition at that time.

The lessons of the Mobilizations, however, have inspired insightful new approaches to political alliance-building across barriers of race and class, initiated in part by a San Francisco Bay Area group called the Movement Generation Justice and Ecology Project.[24] They continued to meet with allied groups, including the Indigenous Environmental Network, the Grassroots Global Justice Alliance and others, to develop a more accountable coalition model. A September 2010 position paper proposed uniting around four themes: root cause remedies; human rights and anti-racism; reparations for historic injustices; and directly democratic control by people over the decisions that affect their lives.[25] In 2012, nearly 30 groups organized as the Climate Justice Alignment (later changed to Alliance) proposed a nationwide campaign for a "just transition" away from fossil fuel dependence, including the creation of millions of new jobs in renewable energy, public transportation, local food, waste reduction, and related areas. As of this writing, the Climate Justice Alliance is engaged in active "just transition" campaigns in Detroit, Richmond, and in the territory of the Navajo nation in the US southwest, and was also planning a People's Climate Justice Summit, featuring frontline community delegations, to follow the massive People's Climate March in New York City in September 2014.[26]

A detailed strategy paper by Jacqueline Patterson, a tireless environmental justice campaigner with the hundred year-old NAACP (National Association for the Advancement of Colored People) in the US systematically outlined the persistent tensions between traditional environmentalists and people organizing in frontline environmental justice communities. While historical and cultural barriers may continue to exist between the two groups, Patterson outlined proposals to overcome those obstacles by forging longer-term working relationships based on mutual concerns, open sharing of resources, and maintaining a stance of "solidarity, not charity." "Empowerment of traditionally disenfranchised groups, ensuring that frontline communities are leading in the relationship, is an essential aim," she wrote.[27] Climate justice activists who actively explore the intersections among various struggles are fond of a quote popularly attributed to the Australian Aboriginal activist and artist, Lila Watson: "If you have come to help me, then you are wasting your time.

But if you have come because your liberation is bound up with mine, then let us work together."[28]

Determined public expressions of climate justice also continue to manifest at the annual UN climate conferences. La Vía Campesina and its affiliated peasant farmer movements were in the forefront of public events in Cancún, Mexico in 2010, actively challenging the limitations of the official proceedings. In Durban, South Africa in 2011, differences between civil society groups participating in the UN conference and those who chose to remain outside came to a head on the very last day during an Occupy Wall Street-styled demonstration just outside the conference hall. While representatives of most international environmental NGOs urged cooperation with UN security in clearing the building of protesters, several activists refused to leave and some were forcibly removed.[29] In Warsaw, Poland in 2013, civil society representatives staged a mass walk-out from the official proceedings, with the support of activists gathered outside. While many groups affiliated with Climate Justice Now have had an increasingly difficult time airing their issues within the UN process—pointing to a concerted effort by officials to marginalize civil society voices—others remain more hopeful about the potential for a coordinated inside/outside strategy around these annual events.

Though various organizational expressions have proved challenging to sustain, the outlook of climate justice continues to have significant appeal in many parts of the world, and the informal Climate Justice Now network remains one point of contact among these disparate currents, especially around the ongoing UN climate negotiations. Between UN conferences, people and groups collaborate through a variety of online forums to share news, debate perspectives and strategies, and further the scope of climate justice organizing. The US-based Grassroots Global Justice Alliance continues to sponsor delegations of US environmental justice activists to the UN climate conferences, while the Labor Network for Sustainability, the Cornell University-sponsored Worker Institute, and others work to raise support for climate justice among the ranks of organized labor in the US and worldwide.[30]

Demands for climate justice have been voiced in recent years by representatives of waste pickers in Durban, South Africa, migrant farmworkers in the hills of Vermont, Rising Tide activists blocking the transport of equipment to ship oily bitumen from the Alberta tar sands, and countless others. Author-activists such as Patrick Bond from South Africa have chronicled the successes of communities engaged in climate justice-inspired organizing throughout Africa, Asia, and Latin America.[31] In many countries, the emerging youth climate movement is carrying out creative direct actions at corporate headquarters, industry conferences, and even at the offices of corporate-friendly environmental groups in the US such as the Environmental Defense Fund and NRDC.[32] The 350.org network, now global in scope, has sought to bring an increased focus on climate justice and grassroots leadership into its activities around the world.

Internationally, people from Pacific Island nations, in some cases already losing land and groundwater to rising seas, remain in the forefront of calls for immediate action. The worldwide confederation of peasant movements, La Via

Campesina, with affiliated groups in more than 80 countries, has challenged the status of carbon as a recently privatized commodity and argued that the UN climate convention "has failed to question the current models of consumption and production based on the illusion of continuous growth."[33] Further, hundreds of cities and towns in the US have defied the federal government's long-standing inaction on climate and committed to substantial, publicly-funded CO_2 reductions of their own. At the local level, people are regenerating local food systems, seeking locally controlled, renewable energy sources, and building solidarity with kindred movements around the world.[34]

Today, the leading edge of climate justice organizing is often with those who are challenging the expansion of extreme forms of fossil fuel extraction around the world. As author Michael Klare, a long-time analyst of energy geopolitics, points out, most current efforts to tap new sources of oil and gas require energy companies "to drill in extreme temperatures or extreme weather, or use extreme pressures, or operate under extreme danger—or some combination of all of these."[35] With readily accessible sources of oil and gas reaching their limits worldwide, industry projections for the future of fossil fuels are increasingly tied to so-called "unconventional" sources, such as tar sands, shale gas, and oil drilled from miles beneath the oceans, including the far reaches of the Arctic. Now that world oil prices have reached over $100 per barrel, technologies such as hydro-fracturing (also known as fracking), horizontal drilling, deepwater drilling, and oil extraction from tar sands—all once seen as hypothetically possible but economically prohibitive—have become central to the fossil fuel industry's plans for the future. Each of these technologies has profound implications for the people and ecosystems most affected by new energy developments, and each has sparked determined opposition from frontline communities and from allies around the world.

Organizing in communities facing extreme energy developments has been inspired in part by the opponents of mountaintop removal coal mining in the US, who have repeatedly put their bodies on the line to expose devastating mining practices that have destroyed over 500 mountains in southern Appalachia. The region has experienced an unprecedented alliance between long-time local residents—many from families that have worked in the coal mines for generations—and youthful forest activists from across the country working with groups such as Coal River Mountain Watch, Climate Ground Zero, Mountain Justice Summer, and Rising Tide. Some of their distinctive action strategies and organizing methods were adopted in part by groups that organized against the construction of the Keystone XL tar sands oil pipeline in Texas and Oklahoma during 2012-13.[36] Another national effort in the US, supported in part by the Sierra Club, helped halt the construction of at least 174 new coal-fired power plants in the US, and others are campaigning to stop the construction of proposed new export terminals for coal, oil and gas.[37] People challenging the rapid expansion of fracking for gas and oil are increasingly well organized, as are mainly indigenous opponents of expanded uranium mining; in Canada, this threat has united opponents from Cree, Dene, Inuit, and other First Nations, from Québec in the east all the way to Nunavut in the far northwest.[38]

It remains to be seen whether these efforts contain the seeds of a fully unified opposition to extreme energy projects throughout North America. Each struggle has its distinctive qualities and unique challenges, and all of the legal, political, and personal issues faced by these campaigners can make it difficult to focus on broader alliance-building efforts. Many groups engaged in local struggles against new energy developments identify rather loosely if at all with a broader climate justice framework. But it is clear that their stories are already having an essential catalytic effect on the broader climate movement, whose centers of activity are often geographically removed from the day-to-day realities of crucial resource-centered struggles.

There is so much more to do. We need to envision a lower-consumption world of decentralized, clean energy and politically empowered communities. Like the antinuclear activists of 30 years ago, who halted the first wave of nuclear power in the US, while articulating an inspiring vision of directly democratic, solar-powered towns and neighborhoods, we need to again dramatize the positive, even utopian, possibilities for a post-petroleum, post-mega-mall world. The technical means clearly exist for a locally-controlled, solar-based alternative, at the same time that dissatisfaction with today's consumption-oriented, highly indebted "American way of life" appears to be at an all time high. Experiments in raising and distributing food more locally are thriving everywhere—as are some efforts toward community-controlled renewable energy production—and enhancing many people's quality of life.

Still, despite the urgency of the problem and the viability of many positive, life-affirming solutions, climate justice activists often find themselves on the defensive, particularly in North America. Greenhouse gas emissions are still rising and environmental disasters continue to unfold from the devastated mountaintops of the Appalachian coal country to the indigenous communities living amidst the tar sands of western Canada. Efforts to create a more unified climate justice movement remain largely under the radar in a political environment still often dominated by reactionary, right wing demagoguery, attacks on organized labor, and increasing economic marginalization of millions of people.

A March 2010 discussion paper from the European Climate Justice Action network suggested one promising approach. "Climate Justice means linking all struggles together that reject neoliberal markets and working towards a world that puts autonomous decision making power in the hands of communities," the paper stated. "We look towards a society which recognizes our historical responsibilities and seeks to protect the global commons, both in terms of the climate and life itself." It concluded, "Fundamentally, we believe that we cannot prevent further global warming without addressing the way our societies are organized—the fight for climate justice and the fight for social justice are one and the same."[39]

In stark contrast to mainstream trends in the US and beyond, many climate justice activists embrace a counter-hegemonic worldview that has often renewed environmentalism since the 1970s: the promise that reorienting societies toward a renewed harmony with nature can help spur a revolutionary transformation of our world. This outlook has helped inspire anti-nuclear activists to sit in at power plant construction sites, forest activists to sustain long-term tree-sits, and environmental justice activists to stand firm in defense of their communities. It has mobilized people around the world to act in solidarity with indigenous peoples fighting resource extraction on their lands. With climate chaos looming on the horizon, such a transformation is no longer optional. Our survival now depends on our ability to renounce the global status-quo and create a more humane and ecologically balanced way of life.

4

Carbon Trading and Other False Solutions

One of the central contributions of the emerging climate justice movement has been to open an evolving conversation about the numerous false solutions to the global climate crisis. From the worldwide expansion of natural gas drilling through technologies of hydrofracking and horizontal drilling to the proliferation of biofuel plantations worldwide, as well as the creation of markets in tradable greenhouse gas emissions permits, elite interests have been promoting nearly everything imaginable as a global warming "solution." Often these claims go hand in hand with efforts to forestall more transformative measures that could actually reduce carbon pollution. Major climate justice groups from the Indigenous Environmental Network to Rising Tide have published comprehensive pamphlets reviewing the myriad false solutions (both in collaboration with the international research group, Carbon Trade Watch),[1] and countless local environmental justice and climate groups have grappled with the local impacts of these measures. As with climate changes overall, the consequences of various false solutions fall disproportionately on marginalized communities that scarcely contribute to the problem of excess greenhouse gas emissions. This chapter will attempt a broad overview of the "false solutions" discussion, offer some historical background, and examine how a thoroughly corporate-driven approach to capping emissions has dominated climate policy discussions in the US.

Indeed since the turn of the 21st century, the world has been inundated with countless seductive, but ultimately false solutions to the threat of catastrophic climate changes. While such measures are put forward by corporations, governments, and many policy analysts as climate solutions, it is clear that they generally present far greater problems than benefits, both for the global environment and locally-affected communities. These false solutions to the climate crisis fall into two broad categories. First are a series of technological interventions that aim to either increase energy supplies while nominally reducing climate pollution, or to intervene on a massive physical scale to counter the warming of the earth's atmosphere. The latter approach, broadly described as "geoengineering," threatens to create a host of new environmental problems in the pursuit of a world-scale techno-fix to the climate crisis.[2] The other broad category of false solutions aims to utilize tools of the capitalist "free market" as a means to reduce pollution. These measures include the creation of regional and national markets in tradable carbon dioxide emissions allowances (often termed "cap-and-trade"), as well as the use of carbon offsets, *i.e.* encouraging investments in nominally low-carbon technologies in other parts of the world as a substitute for reducing an individual or a corporation's own emissions profile.

Which Energy Choices?

Among the many technological false solutions, efforts to expand the use of nuclear power may be the most insidious, as they have been supported by some knowledgeable climate scientists despite nuclear power's inherent flaws. Nuclear power has been subsidized for over fifty years by various governments—amounting to over a hundred billion dollars in the US alone—yet it still presents intractable technical and environmental problems, as revealed yet again by the catastrophic multiple meltdown of nuclear reactors near Fukushima, Japan in 2011. Nuclear scientists and engineers still have no clue what to do with ever-increasing quantities of nuclear waste that will remain highly radioactive for millennia. Any expansion of nuclear power would expose countless more people to the threat of radiation-induced cancer that critical scientists such as Ernest Sternglass have documented since the 1960s, and threaten several indigenous communities with the even more severe consequences of uranium mining and milling. With an estimated 70 per cent of world uranium supplies located underneath indigenous lands, many communities are still experiencing health effects from radiation released during the first uranium boom of the 1970s. There are reportedly over a thousand abandoned uranium mines on Native lands in the American Southwest, where communities have faced epidemics of cancer ever since the earlier wave of mining.[3]

Recent studies of the implications of an expanded nuclear industry have also revealed some new problems. First it appears that supplies of the relatively accessible, high-grade uranium ore that has thus far helped contain the nuclear fuel cycle's greenhouse gas emissions are rather limited. If the nuclear industry ever begins to approach its goal of doubling or tripling world nuclear generating capacity—enough to displace a significant portion of the predicted *growth* in carbon dioxide emissions—they will quickly deplete known reserves of high-grade uranium, and soon have to rely upon fuel sources that require far more fossil fuel energy to mine and purify.[4]

Additionally, the economics of nuclear power rule it out as a significant aid in alleviating the climate crisis. In one recent study, energy systems analyst Amory Lovins compared the current cost of nuclear power to a variety of other sources, both in terms of their power output and their CO_2 emissions savings. He concluded that from 2 to 10 times as much carbon dioxide can be withheld from the atmosphere with comparable investments in wind power, cogeneration (simultaneously extracting electricity and heat from the burning of natural gas), and especially energy efficiency.[5] Efforts to export what is often touted as the most successful example of nuclear development—the French model—have utterly failed, as demonstrated by France's own legacy of nuclear contamination, as well as years of delays, quality-assurance problems, and a near tripling of construction costs at the €9 billion French nuclear construction project in Finland.[6] Such findings, however, are far from adequate to sway either industrialists or politicians who are ideologically committed to the nuclear path. Well known environmental advocates, including the British scientist James Lovelock and *Whole Earth Catalog* founder Stewart Brand, have reaped the unending adoration of the mainstream press for their advocacy for nuclear power, while former US Senator John Kerry offered generous new subsidies to the nuclear industry in his effort to win Republican Senators' support for proposed climate and energy legislation.[7]

Claims that the coal industry may be able to clean up its act and reduce its contribution to the climate crisis are equally fanciful. While politicians promote the false promise of "clean coal," and the World Bank has established a carbon capture trust fund for developing countries, scientists engaged in efforts to capture and sequester CO_2 emissions from coal plants admit that the technology is decades away, at best. Many are doubtful that huge quantities of CO_2 can ever be stored permanently underground, and project that attempting to do so will increase the energy consumed by coal-burning plants by as much as 40 percent to achieve the same energy output.[8] Still, the myth of "cleaner" coal is aggressively promoted in the US and around the world, partly to justify plans to build a new generation of coal-burning plants that are misleadingly marketed as "capture-ready." To make matters worse, CO_2 pumped underground is most often used to add pressure to existing or already-depleted oil wells and thus increase their output, with little examination of how much of the carbon will remain beneath the earth's surface.

The downside of efforts to minimize pollution from coal plants was dramatized by a massive spill of hundreds of millions of gallons of toxic coal ash in 2008, following the breach of a massive dam in the US state of Tennessee. That incident literally buried the valleys below the dam in up to six feet of sludge, which is mainly the byproduct of scrubbers installed to make coal burning somewhat cleaner; contaminants that were once spewed into the air are now contaminating waterways instead. Investigations following the breach of another large coal ash dam in North Carolina in 2014 exposed how that state's entire environmental enforcement apparatus had been redirected to serve coal-dependent utility companies.[9] Another investigation by *New York Times* revealed that more than 300 coal plants violated US water pollution rules during a recent five year period, while only 10 percent of those were fined or sanctioned in any way.[10] People in regions of the Appalachian Mountains that have relied on coal mining for over a century continue to protest the practice of "mountaintop removal" mining, in which mountaintops are literally blasted off to reveal the coal seams below. It is clear that the only way to reduce the climate, environmental, and public health impacts from coal is to further curtail its use.

So-called "biofuels" present a more ambiguous story. On a hobbyist or farm scale, people are running cars and tractors on everything from waste oil from restaurants to homegrown oil from sunflowers. But industrial-scale biofuels present a very different picture; activists in the global South use the more appropriate term, "agrofuels," as these are first and foremost products of global agribusiness. Running American cars on ethanol fermented from corn and European vehicles on diesel fuel pressed from soybeans and other food crops contributed to the worldwide food shortages and price spikes that brought starvation and food riots to at least 35 countries in 2007–08.[11] The amount of corn needed to produce the ethanol for one large SUV tank contains enough calories to feed a hungry person for a year. and researchers have documented an expanding legacy of disturbing environmental and human rights impacts from the development of agrofuels around the world, including a global epidemic of land grabs for biofuel crop production.[12] One study by the International Land Coalition revealed that over 203 million hectares of land was purchased by wealthy overseas interests between 2000 and 2010, with nearly 60 percent aimed toward growing biofuel feedstocks.[13] Those land purchases often result in the expulsion of inhabitants, the loss of food production for local consumption, and sometimes escalate into violent conflicts.

Even if the entire US corn crop were to be used for fuel, it would only displace about 12 percent of domestic gasoline use, according to University of Minnesota researchers.[14] The push for agrofuels has consumed a growing share of US corn—up to 40 percent by 2010—and encouraged growers of less energy and chemical-intensive crops such as wheat and soybeans to transfer more of their acreage to growing corn. Land in the Brazilian Amazon and other fragile regions is being plowed under to grow soybeans for export, while Brazil's uniquely biodiverse coastal grasslands are appropriated to grow sugarcane, today's most efficient source of ethanol. A series of studies beginning in 2008 suggested that the consequences of converting pasture and forest land to the production of fuel crops are severe enough to make most agrofuels net contributors to global warming.[15]

Commercial supplies of biodiesel often come from soybean or canola fields in the US Midwest, Canada, or the Amazon, where these crops are genetically engineered to withstand large doses of chemical herbicides. Increasingly, biodiesel originates from the vast monoculture oil palm plantations that have in recent years displaced more than 80 percent of the native rainforests of Indonesia and Malaysia. As the global food crisis has escalated, some agrofuel proponents suggest that using food crops for fuel is only a temporary solution, and that someday we will run our vehicles on so-called "cellulosic" biofuels extracted from grasses and trees; that myth is exacerbating the widespread conversion of forests to timber plantations, and helping drive a new wave of subsidies to the US biotechnology industry to develop faster-growing genetically engineered trees.[16] Various researchers have documented corporate strategies for advancing a sweeping new "bioeconomy," based on synthetic biology and other recent innovations, and dramatically expanding the biotechnology industry's efforts to commodify all of life on earth.[17]

Trading Pollution

The notion that new commodity markets can become a tool for reducing global emissions of greenhouse gases is perhaps the most brazen expression of capitalist ideology in the climate debate. When Al Gore—then US Vice President— addressed the UN climate conference in Kyoto in 1997, he offered, as we have seen, that the US would sign on to what soon became the Kyoto Protocol under two conditions: that mandated reductions in emissions be far less ambitious than originally proposed, and that emissions reductions be implemented through the market-based trading of "rights to pollute" among various companies and between countries. Under this "cap-and-trade" model, companies are expected to meet a quota for "capping" their emissions; if they fail to do so, they can readily purchase the difference from another permit holder that may have found a way to reduce its emissions faster or more cheaply. While economists claim that this scheme induces companies to implement the most cost-effective changes as soon as possible, experience shows that carbon markets are at least as prone to fraud and manipulation as any other financial markets. More than fifteen years after the Kyoto Protocol was signed, many industrialized countries were still struggling to bring down their annual rate of *increase* in global warming pollution.[18]

The ideological roots of carbon trading go back to the early 1960s, when corporate managers were just beginning to consider the consequences of pollution and resource depletion.[19] Chicago School economist R. H. Coase published a key paper in 1960, where he challenged the widely accepted view of pollution as an economic "externality"— an approach that originated in the 1920s—and proposed a direct equivalence between the harm caused by pollution and the economic loss to polluting entities if they are compelled to curtail production. "The right to do something which has a harmful effect," argued Coase, "is also a factor of production."[20] He proposed that steps to regulate production be evaluated on par with the value of the market transactions that those regulations aim to alter, arguing that economics should determine the optimal allocation of resources needed to best satisfy all parties to any dispute.

The Canadian economist J.H. Dales, widely acknowledged as the founder of pollution trading, carried the discussion two steps further. First, he echoed the neoclassical view that charging for pollution, via a disposal fee or tax, is more efficient than either regulation or subsidizing alternative technologies. Then, as an extension of this argument, Dales proposed a "market in pollution rights" as an administratively simpler and less costly means of implementing pollution charges. "The pollution rights scheme, it seems clear, would require far less policing than any of the others we have discussed," Dales suggested—a proposition thoroughly at odds with the world's experience since Kyoto.[21] In 1972, California Institute of Technology economist David Montgomery presented a detailed mathematical model, purporting to show that a market in licenses to pollute indeed reaches a point of equilibrium at which desired levels of environmental quality are achieved at the lowest possible cost.[22]

By the mid-1970s, the new US Environmental Protection Agency (EPA) was actively experimenting with pollution trading, initially through brokered deals, where the Agency would allow companies to offset pollution from new industrial facilities by reducing existing emissions elsewhere or negotiating with another company to do so. The next significant breakthrough was a 1979 Harvard Law Review article by US Supreme Court Justice (then a law professor) Stephen Breyer. Breyer's article proposed that regulation is only appropriate to replicate the market conditions of a "hypothetically competitive world" and introduced a broader array of policymakers to the concept of "marketable rights to pollute," as a substitute for regulation.[23]

By the late 1980s, Harvard economist Robert Stavins, associated with the uniquely corporate-friendly Environmental Defense Fund, was collaborating with environmentalists, academics, government officials, and representatives of corporations such as Chevron and Monsanto to propose new environmental initiatives to the incoming presidency of the elder George H.W. Bush. These initiatives featured market incentives as a supplement to regulation. Seeking to distance himself from his predecessor Ronald Reagan's rabidly anti-environmental policies, Bush announced a plan based on tradable permits to reduce the sulfur dioxide emissions from power plants that were causing acid rain throughout the eastern US.[24]

Then as now, advocates promoted the idea that the most efficient pollution reductions would come from such emissions trading schemes: the government sets a cap, reduces it over time, and encourages companies to buy and sell pollution permits in order to nominally promote development of the most cost-effective pollution reductions. The Acid Rain Program succeeded modestly, but mainly because regulated electric utilities in the pre-Enron era were mandated by state officials to reduce their output of acid rain-causing sulfur dioxide. Utilities increased their purchases of increasingly available low-sulfur coal, mainly from Western strip-mines. According to many analysts, emissions trading contributed only marginally to the 50 percent pollution reductions from that program. An effort to reduce air pollution in southern California by a similar scheme appeared to mainly delay the installation of emission controls, and that region still has the dirtiest air in the country. In the EPA's Acid Rain Program, trading might have helped reduce the cost of some companies' compliance with the rules, but also may have limited the spread of some promising new pollution control technologies.[25]

That didn't stop the Environmental Defense Fund's senior economist, Daniel Dudek, from proposing that the limited trading of acid rain emissions in the US was an appropriate "scale model" for a much more ambitious plan to trade global emissions of carbon dioxide and other greenhouse gases. Al Gore first endorsed the idea in his best-selling 1992 book, *Earth in the Balance*, and Richard Sandor, then the director of the Chicago Board of Trade, North America's largest commodities market, co-authored a study for UNCTAD (UN Conference on Trade and Development) that endorsed international emissions trading. Sandor went on to found the now-defunct Chicago Climate Exchange, which at its peak engaged nearly 400 international companies and public agencies in a wholly voluntary carbon market.

While the US never adopted the Kyoto Protocol, the rest of the world has had to live with the consequences of Gore's intervention in Kyoto, which created what George Monbiot has aptly termed "an exuberant market in fake emissions cuts."[26] The European Union's Emissions Trading System, for example, created huge new subsidies for highly polluting corporations without corresponding reductions in pollution. In 2006, the value of European carbon allowances plummeted and the carbon trading system almost collapsed under the weight of excess permits that were freely granted to favored industries, and by 2013 the European carbon price was consistently below €5 per ton, leading a broad coalition of environmental groups to propose that the European Trading System was an unmitigated failure and should be abolished. Meanwhile, European countries also directly support energy conservation and renewable energy technologies with public funds, whereas in the US we are told that solar and wind technologies mainly need to prove their viability in the so-called "free market"—in marked contrast to rarely unchallenged subsidies for nuclear power and agrofuels.

Carbon offsets are another central aspect of the "market" approach to global warming, and offer a massive loophole for companies that exceed their share of emissions allowances. These investments in nominally emissions-reducing projects in other parts of the world are a nearly-universal feature of carbon markets, and represent an even greater obstacle to real solutions. Larry Lohmann of the UK's Corner House research group has demonstrated in detail how carbon offset schemes are subsidizing the replacement of native forests by monoculture tree plantations, lengthening the lifespan of polluting industrial facilities and toxic landfills in Asia and Africa in exchange for only incremental changes in their operations, and ultimately perpetuating the very inequalities that must be eliminated if we are to create a more just and sustainable world.[27] Even where offset credits occasionally do help support beneficial projects, they serve to postpone investments in necessary emissions reductions in the North and represent a gaping hole in any mandated "cap" in carbon dioxide emissions. At best, they maintain current emissions levels; at worst, they make it possible for domestic emissions in Northern countries to continue to rise. Offsets are a means for polluting industries to continue business as usual at home while contributing, marginally at best, to emission reductions elsewhere.

In the late 2000s, individual purchases of carbon offsets became the basis for a lucrative new business in their own right. Online purchases of tickets for air travel and some major cultural events were routinely accompanied by pleas to purchase offsets to alleviate one's personal contribution to global warming. These are aptly compared to the "indulgences" that sinners used to buy from the Catholic church during the Middle Ages. On a global scale, with corporations instead of individuals as the main players, offsets became a problem of gigantic proportions. Rather than promoting innovative measures to reduce energy use and sequester carbon in poor countries, as they are usually advertised, carbon offsets instead have subsidized tree plantations in the tropics, methane capture from expanding toxic landfills, minor retooling of highly polluting pig iron smelters in India, and even the routine destruction of byproducts from China's expanding production of ozone-destroying hydrofluorocarbons.[28]

One of the most notorious cases was that of the French chemical company, Rhodia, which reaped nearly a billion dollars in carbon offset credits in exchange for a $15 million investment in 1970s-vintage technology to destroy the potent greenhouse gas nitrous oxide in its facility in South Korea.[29] Carbon offsets became the company's most profitable line of business. Major hydroelectric projects, mainly in China, India and Brazil, represented a quarter of all applications for credits through the UN's offset program, the so-called Clean Development Mechanism, and nearly all of these were already under development before they applied for their credits. As the International Rivers Network and others have pointed out, large-scale hydro, far from being green, is responsible for huge quantities of methane and other greenhouse gases.[30] A German study of UN-approved carbon offset projects in 2007 reported that as many as 86 percent of all offset-funded projects would likely have been carried out anyway.[31] This ran counter to the Kyoto Protocol's guideline requiring that projects granted emissions offsets must be "additional," that is the qualifying projects cannot already be underway.

Nearly two decades of experience has shown that capitalist techno-fixes, trading and offsets will not likely usher in the zero-emissions future that we know is both necessary and achievable. Nevertheless, markets in greenhouse gas emissions allowances continue to be a central feature of proposed climate policies in the US and worldwide.

False Solutions in the US Congress

When the US House of Representatives passed a first-ever climate bill in June of 2009, it was received by the mainstream press, and many environmentalists, with a palpable sense of triumph. Representative Henry Waxman of California, one of the bill's main sponsors, called it a "decisive and historic action," and President Obama described the bill as "a bold and necessary step." Fred Krupp of the Environmental Defense Fund (EDF) called it no less than "the most important environmental and energy legislation in the history of our country."

EDF, along with the Natural Resources Defense Council (NRDC) and the Nature Conservancy, played a central role in the development of the 2009-'10 climate bill. As initiators of the US Climate Action Partnership, a collaboration with highly polluting corporations such as Alcoa, BP, Dow, DuPont, GE, and the former "big three" US automakers, among others, they articulated what would become the bill's broad outlines: an emphasis on long-range goals, trading of emissions allowances, initially free distribution of those allowances to polluting corporations, and a generous offset provision that permits companies to defer significant pollution reductions well into the future.[32]

While many environmentalists suggested that any step in the direction of regulating carbon dioxide and other climate damaging greenhouse gases is better than nothing, others remained skeptical. Friends of the Earth, Public Citizen, and Greenpeace issued sharp critiques of the bill's focus on corporate-friendly cap-and-trade measures. Even more scathing were analyses from smaller independent groups such as Chesapeake Climate Action, Climate SOS, and the influential Arizona-based Center for Biological Diversity. The bill that passed the House in 2009 fell far short of international standards in mandating a meaningful level of reductions in global warming pollution, and relied heavily on market-based emissions-trading, especially in the longer-term. It also contained a number of Trojan Horse provisions that would likely forestall, rather than encourage, genuine climate progress.

By the time the bill had passed through the relevant committees, as well as last-minute horse-trading on the House floor, the loopholes were staggering to behold. Most analysts by then agreed that greenhouse gas emissions on the order of 20-40 percent were needed within a decade or so to prevent a slide toward uncontrollable global climate chaos, with reductions on the order of 80-95 percent for the leading industrial economies required by mid-century. The House bill first attempted to shift the terms of the discussion by measuring emissions relative to 2005 levels rather than the accepted Kyoto Protocol benchmark of 1990. It promised a 17 percent reduction by 2020, relative to 2005, which only translates into 4 or 5 percent less global warming pollution than the US produced in 1990. This was the nominal basis for the US negotiating position in Copenhagen, and was promoted by President Obama as his administration's central climate goal for many years afterward. The much-touted cap-and-trade provision of the bill accounted for only a 1 percent reduction by 2020, according to the Center for Biological Diversity's analysis, with the remainder coming from traditional performance standards for smaller pollution sources, including automobiles, and from a controversial USAID effort to reduce deforestation in poorer countries. For comparison, recall that most wealthy countries agreed more than fifteen years ago in Kyoto to reduce their emissions to 6-8 percent below 1990 levels by 2012.

The deforestation provisions of the bill mirrored a highly controversial international climate mitigation strategy, promoted by the UN and the World Bank under the name of Reducing Emissions from Deforestation and Forest Degradation (REDD). REDD mainly targets intact forested lands, largely occupied by indigenous peoples, which are now threatened with privatization for use as carbon offsets.[33]

Soon after the climate bill passed the House, an Anglo-African brokerage firm announced that it would sell "avoided deforestation" credits to buyers of voluntary carbon offsets in the US, threatening a new wave of corporate takeovers of African forest lands.

Under the House bill, some 7400 facilities across the US would receive annual allowances to continue emitting carbon dioxide and other greenhouse gases.[34] As many as 85 percent of the allowances would initially go to polluting companies for free, reversing Obama's 2008 campaign pledge that they should mainly be auctioned off. (In Europe, utilities routinely bill their customers for these annually acquired new assets.) Meanwhile, the quantity of available pollution allowances would have increased for several years, only falling gradually thereafter, and companies would be allowed to indefinitely "bank" them for future use, borrow from their future allocations, and trade allowances on the open market with other companies as well as with Wall Street firms and an emerging cadre of brokers in carbon futures. For many observers, this was highly reminiscent of the financial machinations that nearly brought down the world's financial markets just a year earlier; meanwhile carbon market boosters were projecting a worldwide trading system that would eventually be valued at $10 trillion a year—sufficient to launch yet another destabilizing financial bubble.

The bill's supporters argued that, for all their uncertainty, these highly manipulable financial measures are worth the risk because they facilitate the phase-in of an enforceable cap on global warming pollution. But the legislation replicated another of the most egregious features of the Kyoto Protocol:

a virtual "hole in the cap," in the form of an offset feature that allows companies to meet their obligations without reducing their own emissions at home, but rather by investing in pollution control projects anywhere in the country and even overseas. Companies would have been able to satisfy their full obligation to reduce CO_2 by buying offsets until 2027; those familiar with the bill's fine print suggested that companies could stretch this out for 30-40 years.

Allowing companies to postpone their own greenhouse gas reductions by buying offsets was one Trojan Horse provision in the climate bill that threatened future climate progress. Another such measure would have largely prohibited the EPA from using the Clean Air Act to establish future regulation of greenhouse gas emissions. It is important to note it was a 2007 Supreme Court decision allowing the EPA to regulate greenhouse gases as a pollutant that finally forced the G.W. Bush administration to start talking about global warming. Removing this authority represented a defining concession to polluting industries, one that would have virtually removed any teeth of enforcement from future measures to forestall climate chaos. It would become one of the main reasons that so many US environmentalists ultimately refused to support the bill, and instead encouraged the Obama administration to base its climate policies on the Clean Air Act's regulatory mandates.

Still, these damaging measures built into the climate bill weren't enough to assuage corporate lobbyists, so politically powerful industries were allowed to write in even more concessions. (The Center for Public Integrity reported in early 2009 that some 2340 lobbyists were working in Washington on this issue.[35]) The coal industry would have until 2025 to comply with the bill's mandated pollution reductions, with ample means for gaining further extensions. Agribusiness, which is responsible for as much as a quarter of US greenhouse gas emissions, was exempt from most of the bill's provisions, but large scale farmers who reduce tillage by growing crops genetically engineered to withstand megadoses of herbicides would be eligible for offset credits paid for by industrial polluters. Assessments of ethanol's eligibility as a "renewable fuel" would exclude its effects on land use, a factor that researchers from Princeton University and the University of Minnesota proved decisive in a pair of landmark studies, showing how industrial biofuels are often net contributors to global warming when impacts from land use changes are included in the assessments.[36] Finally, the nuclear industry expected to be a leading beneficiary of the bill's free allocation of emission allowances; a memo leaked to the *Huffington Post* reported that Exelon, the largest US nuclear power company, expected a $1-1.5 billion annual windfall from the bill.[37] This despite the problem of greenhouse gas emissions throughout the nuclear fuel cycle. With horse-trading continuing on the House floor right up to the time of the vote, the bill ultimately included billions of dollars in "special-interest favors," according to the *New York Times*.[38] These included $1 billion for green jobs programs in low income communities, viewed as a small concession to inner city environmental justice activists; the biggest favors were clearly reserved for oil, coal and gas producers.

Senators John Kerry and Barbara Boxer eventually released a Senate version of the climate bill, nominally developed in collaboration with Republican and independent colleagues.

In the hope of gaining more bipartisan support, their bill included even more blatant giveaways to the fossil fuel, coal and nuclear industries. This bill's excesses were so egregious that several environmental groups that had expressed a skeptical but conciliatory view toward the House bill were far more willing to speak out in opposition to Kerry's version; many veteran political observers pronounced the Senate bill "dead on arrival."

While Kerry's giveaways to the energy industry were too much even for some believers in environmental "consensus" and market-based carbon trading, Senate Republicans still boycotted the first committee hearing that was convened to address the proposal. Kerry shifted his focus toward crafting an even more "bipartisan" compromise, in collaboration with Connecticut Senator Joe Lieberman, a notorious "independent" war hawk, and South Carolina Republican Lindsey Graham. One of the first public announcements of this unlikely collaboration was a *New York Times* opinion piece in which Kerry and Graham called for streamlining regulation of nuclear power and expanding offshore oil drilling.[39] Even after BP's catastrophic oil spill in the Gulf of Mexico, the bill continued to offer huge new concessions to oil companies seeking to drill offshore. Kerry stated publicly that the EPA's authority to regulate greenhouse gases would be leveraged as a bargaining chip to help gain more Republican support for his bill.

While some Washington insiders believed that these giveaways might help rally corporate support for a climate bill, President Obama went ahead and offered up many of the Kerry's team's bargaining chips even before the Senate began its debate. Obama's early 2010 budget proposal included nearly $55 billion in new loan guarantees for the nuclear industry. In late March, he offered a nationwide expansion of offshore oil drilling, a plan that was withdrawn only after BP's massive oil spill in the Gulf of Mexico. According to Ryan Lizza of the *New Yorker*, there was no coordination with Senate staffers around these proposals; instead, "Obama had now given away what the senators were planning to trade."[40] Officials in the Obama White House also apparently sabotaged a pending deal with the oil companies to streamline their purchases of emissions permits; a White House staffer's leak to Fox News turned the deal into political poison for Graham by recasting the carbon credits as equivalent to a gas tax. An alternative bipartisan proposal, offered by senators from Washington State and from Maine, was praised by many environmentalists as it featured a substantially more progressive plan to tax CO_2 emissions and also returned rebates or "dividends" to taxpayers; however this proposal received little serious consideration.

A 2013 study of the 2009-10 US climate debate by Harvard University sociologist Theda Skocpol correctly placed much of the blame for the larger climate bill's demise on the excessively corporate-friendly approach advocated by EDF and USCAP. By attempting to enlist the most polluting corporations on their side, and largely neglecting a broad range of political and even business interests that might benefit from meaningful climate legislation, they ended up promoting a bill that hardly anyone could enthusiastically support. The effort was further sabotaged by political consultants urging the bill's advocates to only speak in the most euphemistic terms about global warming, focusing instead on "'green jobs,' 'threats to public health,' and the need to 'reduce dependence on foreign oil to bolster national defense.'"[41] The increasing political divide around environmental issues in the US renders the notion of a non-partisan advocacy for cap-and-trade legislation as "a dangerous fantasy" that drives proponents to "misunderstand the political realities they must face," wrote Skocpol.[42]

A few years later, the Obama administration's record on climate issues remained mixed at best. Rhetorically, Obama has maintained a forthright emphasis on the significance of climate change along with an appropriately sarcastic stance toward the climate denialists who have shaped the official posture of congressional Republicans. The administration also raised the fuel efficiency standards that automobile manufacturers must comply with to an average of 54.5 miles per gallon of gasoline (by 2025), a process that had been stalled since 1990. As of this writing, Obama has continued to delay construction of the northern portion of the notorious Keystone XL oil pipeline, which would transport 830,000 barrels of heavy bituminous material every day from the tar sands fields of Alberta, Canada to Gulf of Mexico oil refineries. However, he has also presided over an expansion of US infrastructure for transporting, processing, and perhaps soon exporting fossil fuels; such a pace of fossil fuel infrastructure expansion has not been seen since the 1950s. Obama's "all of the above" energy strategy encourages the development of solar and wind energy, but mainly emphasizes expanded production of natural gas through hydrofracking, new loan guarantees for nuclear power, and continued granting of new leases for offshore oil exploration.

In June of 2014, Obama announced a new proposal aimed at reducing CO_2 emissions from the electric power sector, particularly from older coal-fired power plants that have long been exempted from key requirements of the Clean Air Act. While headlines emphasized the overall goal of reducing power plant emissions by 30 percent by 2030, the details left much to be desired. First, the end goal is overly modest, as utilities had already reduced emissions by half that amount since the policy's baseline year of 2005. This was largely a product of the economic recession and continuing stagnation, coupled with successful local opposition to most newly proposed coal plants; coal use in the US fell by nearly 20 percent in just a few short years.

Second, the plan calculated a goal for each state to reduce its emissions intensity—CO_2 per unit of power production—so states with growing economies could still increase their overall emissions while meeting the plan's requirements. Each state's goal was to be based on four key benchmarks: a modest improvement in the efficiency of its coal-burning facilities, a rising capacity for gas-fueled generation, modest annual increases in energy efficiency, and efforts to sustain recent trends in renewable energy development.[43] States that have difficulty meeting those goals would be encouraged to trade emissions with other states, and subsidies were offered for such perverse measures as prolonging the life of economically unviable nuclear power plants. The overall 30 percent goal is merely an estimate of the emissions reductions that could result from fully implementing these policies; the details will likely shift significantly as policymakers respond to public comments and probable lawsuits. All indications are that this will prove to be yet another example of doing far too little, and far too late, to address the full magnitude of the climate crisis.

Today it is clearer than ever that a much more forward-looking, even revolutionary approach is necessary to reduce climate-destabilizing pollution and achieve meaningful steps toward a fossil fuel-free economy. Such a transition threatens the global economy's most powerful corporate empires; indeed the very shape of modern capitalism is a product of fossil fuel expansion and is sustained by the myth of unlimited "cheap energy." Not only is the evolution of the economic system historically inseparable from the exploitation of fossil fuels but, as a recent report from the UK's Corner House research group explains, "the entire contemporary system of making profits out of labor depended absolutely on cheap fossil carbon..."[44] To meaningfully challenge this system requires not only a resolute opposition to the expansion of fossil fuel infrastructure, but a rethinking of the underlying assumptions and beliefs of our society, a goal the remainder of this book aims to illuminate and encourage.

5

On Utopian Aspirations in the Climate Movement

It can be difficult to closely follow developments in climate science without simultaneously falling prey to a rather grim, even apocalyptic view of the future. Predictions of impending disaster look more severe with every new wave of extreme weather and each new study of the effects of the rising levels of greenhouse gases in the earth's atmosphere. Steadily rising levels of drought, wildfires and floods have been experienced on all the earth's inhabited continents, and people in the tropics and subtropics already face far more difficulty growing enough food due to increasingly unstable weather patterns. Studies predict increasing mass migrations of people desperate to escape the worst consequences of widespread climate disruptions. And persistent diplomatic gridlock and obstruction at the UN level has raised the possibility that temperature increases could even exceed 10°C in the Arctic and in parts of Africa.[1]

In this context, the utopian ecological visions that inspired earlier generations of environmental activists can seem quaint and out-of-date. The images of autonomous, self-reliant, solar-powered cities and towns that illuminated the first large wave of anti-nuclear activism in the 1970s and eighties sometimes feel more distant than ever. Since those years, we have seen an unprecedented flowering of local food systems, natural building, permaculture design, urban ecology, and other important innovations that first emerged from that earlier wave of activism. Yet today's advocates of local self reliance and ecological lifestyles seem to engage only on rare occasions in the political struggles that are necessary to advance their visions for a better future.

For social ecologists seeking to further the forward-looking, reconstructive dimensions of an ecological world view, this presents a serious dilemma. From the 1960s onward, Murray Bookchin, the founding theorist of social ecology, proposed that the critical, holistic outlook of ecological science was logically and historically linked to a radically transformative vision for society. A fundamental rethinking of human societies' relationship to the natural world, he proposed, is made imperative by the understandings of ecological science, furthering the potential for a revolutionary transformation of both our philosophical assumptions and our political and social institutions. Can this approach to ecology, politics and history be renewed for our time? What kinds of social movements have the potential to express these possibilities? Can we meaningfully address the simultaneous threats of climate chaos and potential social breakdown while renewing and further developing the revolutionary outlook of social ecology?

Ecology and Capitalism

From the 1960s until his passing in 2006, Murray Bookchin insisted that the ecological crisis was a fundamental threat to capitalism, due to the system's built in necessity to continuously expand its scope and its spheres of control. In a 2001 reflection on the origins of social ecology, Bookchin wrote:

> I was trying to provide a viable substitute for Marx's defunct economic imperative, namely an *ecological imperative* that, if thought out [...] would show that *capitalism stood in an irreconcilable contradiction with the natural world* [...] In short, precisely because capitalism was, *by definition*, a competitive and commodity-based economy, it would be compelled to turn the complex into the simple and give rise to a planet that was incompatible environmentally with advanced life forms. The growth of capitalism was incompatible with the evolution of biotic complexity *as such*—and certainly, with the development of human life and the evolution of human society.[2] [emphasis in original]

For a couple of decades, however, it appeared to many that capitalism had found a way to accommodate non-human nature and perhaps to "green" itself. This notion can be traced to the period leading up to the 20th anniversary of the first Earth Day. By the spring of 1990, many of the largest, most notoriously polluting corporations had begun to incorporate environmental messages into their advertising. By reducing waste, partially restoring damaged ecosystems, investing in renewable energy, and promoting an idealized environmental ethic, the oil, chemical, and other highly polluting industries would portray themselves as stewards of the environment. Prominent authors promised a "sustainable," even "natural" capitalism, whereby production and consumption would continue to grow and large corporations could join with a new generation of "green" entrepreneurs to solve our environmental problems.[3]

As awareness of the climate crisis rose together with the cost of energy during 2006-7, the "green consumerism" that was promoted as a conscientious lifestyle choice in the 1990s became an all-encompassing mass culture phenomenon. Mainstream lifestyle and even fashion magazines featured special "green" issues, and the *New York Times* reported that 35 million Americans were regularly seeking out (often high-priced) "earth-friendly" products, "from organic beeswax lipstick from the west Zambian rain forest to Toyota Priuses."[4] But the *Times* acknowledged rising criticism of the trend as well, quoting the one-time "green business" pioneer Paul Hawken as saying, "Green consumerism is an oxymoronic phrase," and acknowledging that truly green living might indeed require buying less. With rising awareness of the cost of manufacturing new "green" products, even the iconic Prius was criticized for the high energy costs embedded in its manufacture.

More forward-looking capitalists have had to admit in recent years that an increasingly chaotic natural and social environment will necessarily limit business opportunities.[5] Some critics have suggested that this is one underlying reason for the increasing growth and influence of the financial sector:

> In its disciplinary zeal, capitalism has so undermined the ecological conditions of so many people that a state of global ungovernability has developed, further forcing investors to escape into the mediated world of finance where they hope to make hefty returns without bodily confronting the people they need to exploit. But this exodus has merely deferred the crisis, since "ecological" struggles are being fought all over the planet and are forcing an inevitable increase in the cost of future constant capital.[6]

The result is an increasingly parasitic form of capitalism, featuring widening discrepancies in wealth, both worldwide and within most countries, and the outsourcing of production to the countries and regions where labor costs and environmental enforcement are at the lowest possible levels. As the profitability of socially useful production has fallen precipitously, we have seen the emergence of a casino-like "shadow" economy, in which a rising share of society's material resources are squandered by elites in the pursuit of socially parasitic but highly lucrative profits from ever-more exotic financial manipulations.[7]

As we have seen, numerous questionable responses to the threat of climate change have emerged from this political and economic context. The previous chapter addressed the consequences of both technological false solutions and those derived from the machinations of financial markets. Different sectors of industrial and finance capital favor differing variations on the general theme, but the overarching message is that solutions to global warming are at hand and everyone should simply go on consuming. More hopeful innovations in solar and wind technology, "smart" power grids, and even energy saving technologies are promoted by some "green" capitalists as well, but these technologies continue to be marginalized by the prevailing financial and political system, raising serious questions about how such alternatives can be implemented.

A Utopian Movement?

The last time a forward-looking popular movement in the US compelled widespread changes in environmental and energy policies was during the late 1970s. In the aftermath of the OPEC oil embargo, imposed during the 1973 Arab-Israeli war, the nuclear and utility industries adopted a plan to construct more than 300 nuclear power plants in the United States by the year 2000. Utility and state officials identified rural communities across the US as potential sites for new nuclear facilities, and the popular response was swift and unanticipated. A powerful grassroots antinuclear movement emerged, and in April of 1977, over 1400 people were arrested trying to nonviolently occupy a nuclear construction site in the coastal town of Seabrook, New Hampshire. That event helped inspire the emergence of decentralized, grassroots antinuclear alliances all across the country, committed to nonviolent direct action, horizontal forms of internal organization, and a sophisticated understanding of the relationship between technological and social changes. Not only did these groups adopt an uncompromising call for "No Nukes," but many promoted a vision of an entirely new social order, rooted in decentralized, solar-powered communities empowered to decide both their energy future and their political future. If the nuclear state almost inevitably leads to a police state—due to the massive security apparatus necessary to protect hundreds of nuclear plants and radioactive waste facilities all over the country—activists proposed that a solar-based energy system could provide the underpinning for a radically decentralized and directly democratic model for society.

This movement was so successful in raising the hazards of nuclear power as a matter of urgent public concern that nuclear power projects all across the US faced cancellation. When the nuclear reactor at Three Mile Island near Harrisburg, Pennsylvania partially melted down in March of 1979, it spelled the end of the nuclear expansion. No new nuclear plants were licensed or built in the United States for more than 30 years after Three Mile Island. The antinuclear movement of the late 1970s also helped spawn the first significant development of solar and wind technologies, aided by substantial but temporary tax benefits for solar installations, and helped launch a visionary "green cities" movement that captured the imaginations of architects, planners and ordinary citizens alike.

The 1970s and early eighties were relatively hopeful times, and utopian thinking was far more widespread than it is today. This was prior to the "Reagan revolution" in US politics and the rise of neoliberalism worldwide. The political right had not quite begun its crusade to depict the former Soviet Union as the apotheosis of utopian social engineering gone awry. Many antinuclear activists looked to the emerging outlook of social ecology and the writings of its founding theorist, Murray Bookchin, as a source of theoretical grounding for a revolutionary ecological politics. Social ecology challenged activists by overturning prevailing views about the evolution of social and cultural relationships to non-human nature and examining the roots of domination in the earliest emergence of human social hierarchies. For the activists of that period, Bookchin's insistence that environmental problems are fundamentally social and political in origin encouraged forward-looking responses to ecological concerns and reconstructive visions of a fundamentally transformed society. Social ecology's emphasis on popular power and direct democracy continued to inspire activists in the global justice movement of the 1990s and early 2000s, as well as the Occupy movement more recently.

While radically reconstructive social visions are far less prevalent in today's social and political climate, dissatisfaction with the status quo is wide-reaching throughout many sectors of the population. The more people consume, and the deeper they fall into debt, the less satisfied they are with the world of business-as-usual. Though elite discourse and the corporate media continue to be confined by a narrowly circumscribed status-quo, there is also the potential for a new opening, reaching far beyond the narrow limits of what is now deemed politically "acceptable."

Activists hesitant to question the underlying assumptions of capitalism tend to focus on various techno-fixes. While these are generally far more benign than the false solutions proposed by the coal, nuclear and agrofuel industries, they are inherently limited in the absence of broader, systemic changes. Clearly, such proposals are often compelling on their own terms. For example, the acclaimed advocate Van Jones, who advised the Obama White House on green jobs policies before he fell victim to a vicious attack from right wing media apparatus in the US, suggests that:

> Hundreds of thousands of green-collar jobs will be weatherizing and energy-retrofitting every building in the United States. Buildings with leaky windows, ill-fitting doors, poor insulation and old appliances can gobble up 30 percent more energy [...] Drafty buildings create broke, chilly people—and an overheated planet.[8]

Clearly, practical measures to address these problems will offer an important benefit for those most in need, and are an essential step toward a greener future. But can such near-term measures be sufficient? In technical terms, there is no shortage of feasible solutions to ending excessive energy consumption and rapidly curtailing the use of fossil fuels. For example since the 1970s, Rocky Mountain Institute founder Amory Lovins has been a tireless advocate for dramatically increased energy efficiency throughout the US and global economies. He has demonstrated in exhaustive detail how we can feasibly reduce energy consumption by at least 40 percent, and how many promising changes in technology will result in an unambiguous economic gain. In a recent book, he projected that the US can reduce CO_2 emissions by 85 percent over 40 years with a \$4.5 trillion total investment and achieve net savings of $5 trillion in energy costs.[9] Lovins' pitch is unapologetically aimed at believers in the "free market" and those whose primary concern is market profitability, yet the market's adoption of his ideas has been spotty at best. Mark Jacobson's research group at Stanford University has developed detailed proposals for replacing all new energy with wind, water and solar power by 2030 and the world's entire energy supply by 2050.[10]

A central problem, however, is that capitalism aims to maximize profits, not efficiency. Indeed, economists since the 19th century have suggested that improvements in the efficiency of resource consumption often tend to *increase* demand as capitalists learn how to do more with less, while continuing to grow the economy.[11] Richard York from the University of Oregon has calculated that just a quarter of non-fossil energy currently replaces fossil fuels, and only a tenth of non-fossil electricity; the rest is simply adding more new capacity to the system.[12] While efficiency improvements can significantly reduce the costs of production, corporations will generally accept the added cost of sustaining existing methods that have proven to keep profits growing. Corporations almost invariably prefer to lay off workers, outsource production, or move factories overseas than to invest in environmentally meaningful improvements in production methods. The *New York Times* reported that corporations are hesitant to invest in measures to save energy and make their operations more efficient unless they can demonstrate a two year payback—a constraint rarely imposed on other forms of investment.[13] Lovins' focus on efficiency runs counter to the inclinations of a business world aggressively oriented toward growth, capital mobility and accumulation. While important innovations in solar technology, for example, are announced almost daily, its acceptance in the capitalist marketplace still falls far behind many other, far more speculative and hazardous alternatives.

Hope and Despair

If technological fixes are insufficient to usher in an age of renewable technologies, is the situation hopeless? Is a nihilistic response, anticipating a cataclysmic "end of civilization" as suggested by several popular authors today, the only viable alternative? Are we limited to a future of defensive battles against an increasingly authoritarian world of scarcity and climate chaos? Or can the prefigurative, forward-looking dimensions of earlier, more hopeful radical ecological movements be renewed in our time?

Dystopian outlooks are clearly on the rise in popular culture, among environmentally-minded radicals, and in much of the anti-authoritarian left today. "Anarchists and their allies are now required to project themselves into a future of growing instability and deterioration," writes Israeli activist and scholar Uri Gordon. He acknowledges the current flowering of permaculture and other sustainable technologies as a central aspect of today's experiments toward "community self-sufficiency," but views these as "rear guard" actions, best aimed to "encourage and protect the autonomy and grassroots orientation of emergent resistances" in a fundamentally deteriorating social and political climate.[14]

Derrick Jensen, one of the most prolific and popular anti-authoritarian writers in recent years, insists that a rational transition to an ecologically sustainable society is impossible, and that the only sensible role for ecologically aware activists is to help bring on the collapse of Western civilization. Hope itself, for Jensen, is "a curse and a bane," an acceptance of powerlessness, and ultimately "what keeps us chained to the system." Well before Barack Obama adopted a vaguely defined "Hope" as a theme of his first presidential campaign, Jensen argued that hope "serves the needs of those in power as surely as belief in a distant heaven; that hope is really nothing more than a secular way of keeping us in line."[15]

This view is considerably at odds with many decades of historical scholarship and activist praxis. Radical despair may be sufficient to motivate some young activists to confront authorities when necessary, but it seems unlikely to be able to sustain the lifetimes of radical thought and action that are necessary if we are to create a different world. As social movement historian Richard Flacks has shown, most people are only willing to disrupt the patterns of their daily lives to engage in the project he terms "making history" when social grievances become personal, and they have a tangible sense that a better way is possible. This, for Flacks, is among the historic roles of democratic popular movements, to further the idea "that people are capable of and ought to be making their own history, that the making of history ought to be integrated with everyday life, that [prevailing] social arrangements […] can and must be replaced by frameworks that permit routine access and participation by all in the decisions that affect their lives."[16]

Flacks' expansive view of democracy resonates well with social ecology's long-range, community-centered vision (see Chapter 6). Bookchin's reconstructive outlook is rooted in direct democracy, in confederations of empowered communities challenging the hegemony of capital and the state, and in restoring a sense of reciprocity to economic relationships, which are ultimately subordinated to the needs of the community. His view resonates with economic historian Karl Polanyi's piercing analysis of the origins of the mythical "self-regulating" market and its imposed separation of economics from society.[17] Bookchin viewed the subordination of economics as an essential step toward restoring harmony to human relations, and to the reharmonization of our communities with non-human nature.

Further, in his 1970s and eighties' anthropological studies, Bookchin sought to draw out a number of ethical principles common to preliterate, or "organic" societies, that could further illuminate the path toward such a reharmonization. These include anthropologist Paul Radin's concept of the irreducible minimum—the idea that communities are responsible for satisfying their members' most basic human needs—and an expanded view of social complementarity, where communities accept responsibility to compensate for differences among individuals, helping assure that variations in skill or ability in particular areas will not serve to rationalize the emergence of new forms of hierarchy.[18]

Rather than prescribing blueprints for a future society, Bookchin sought to educe principles from the broad scope of human history that he saw as expressing potentialities for further human development. His outlook on social change is resonant with the best of the utopian tradition, as described in a recent essay by Randall Amster, who describes utopia as

> a dynamic *process* and not a static *place* [...] attaining a harmonious exchange with nature and an open, participatory process among community members are central features of these [utopian] endeavors; that resistance to dominant cultures of repression and authoritarianism is a common impetus for anarcho-utopian undertakings; and that communities embodying these principles are properly viewed as ongoing experiments and not finished products.[19]

While people of different material circumstances and cultural backgrounds would surely emphasize differing needs and inclinations in their search for a better society, such a long-range utopian outlook can help us comprehend the fullest scope of human possibilities.

This view has far more to offer than a bleak "end of civilization" outlook, both for people in Northern countries facing increasingly chaotic weather and for people around the world who are experiencing more extreme consequences of climate disruptions. It is the hope for a better society, along with the determination and support necessary to intervene to challenge current inequities, that has inspired movements of land-based peoples around the world to refuse to accept an oppressive status quo and act to take the future into their hands.

Still, since the collapse of the authoritarian, nominally socialist bloc of countries that was dominated by the Soviet Union and spanned nearly all of eastern Europe, many authors have cast doubt on all forms of radical speculation about the future. Utopian political thought—with its legacy reaching back to Plato and to the writings of Thomas More in the early 16th century—is now seen by many as thoroughly discredited. Liberal centrists, as well as ideologues of the political right tend to dismiss the pursuit of any comprehensive alternative political outlook as if it were merely a potential stepping stone to tyranny. Even forward-looking thinkers such as the literary critic Frederic Jameson suggest that utopia "had come to designate a program which neglected human frailty" implying "the ideal purity of a perfect system that always had to be imposed by force on its imperfect and reluctant subjects."[20]

This is in stark contrast to the view of Ernst Bloch, the mid-20th century chronicler of the utopian tradition who, instead, in Jameson's words, "posits a Utopian impulse governing everything future-oriented in life and culture."[21] Bloch's exhaustive and free-ranging three-volume work, *The Principle of Hope* begins with the simple act of daydreaming, and then embarks on an epic journey through the myriad expressions of the utopian impulse throughout Western history, spanning folktales, the arts and literature, along with the perennial search for a better world. "Fraudulent hope is one of the greatest malefactors, even enervators of the human race," states Bloch, while "concretely genuine hope its most dedicated benefactor."[22]

Current scholarship on this tradition often views utopia as a central element in the emergence of a secular social order in the West, marking the decline of religion as the sole means for expressing people's hopes for the future. French social critic Alain Touraine writes, "Utopia was born only when the political order separated from the cosmological or religious order ... Utopia is one of the products of secularization."[23] Utopian scholar Lyman Sargent quotes the Dutch future studies pioneer Frederick Polak, who wrote in 1961:

> ... if Western man now stops thinking and dreaming the materials of new images of the future and attempts to shut himself up in the present, out of longing for security and for fear of the future, his civilization will come to an end. He has no choice but to dream or to die, condemning the whole of Western society to die with him.[24]

The pioneering German sociologist Karl Mannheim wrote that "The utopian mentality is at the base of all serious social change" and saw the integrity of human will as resting to a large part on "the reality-transcending power of utopia."[25] While the popular literature of the century wavers continually between the poles of utopia and dystopia, even many intellectuals who lived through the nightmare of Stalinism and its decline warn against discarding utopia along with the baggage of the 20th century authoritarian left. For example the Czech dissident Milan Simecka, who experienced the repression of the Prague Spring of 1968, writes that "A world without utopias would be a world without social hope, a world of resignation to the status quo and the devalued slogans of everyday political life."[26] Today, if we fail to sustain the legacy of utopia, not only will we miss the opportunity to envision and actualize a humane, post-capitalist, post-petroleum future, but we may inadvertently surrender humanity's future to the false hopes of an ascendant religious fundamentalism.

The social critic Immanuel Wallerstein is one who has recently sought to rescue utopian thinking from its role as a breeder "of illusions, and therefore, inevitably, of disillusions," proposing a renewed "utopistics," which broadly examines the alternatives and reveals "the substantive rationality of alternative possible historical systems."[27] Wallerstein is one renowned contemporary social theorist who explicitly speaks to the likelihood of a difficult, contentious and unpredictable, but potentially rational and democratic long-term transition to a post-capitalist world. It is in this spirit of exploring rational, liberatory future possibilities that Murray Bookchin developed and elaborated his theory of social ecology, and today's climate activists are seeking to define the terms of a world beyond petro-capitalism. In the next chapter, we will turn to elaborating the holistic revolutionary outlook of social ecology and its numerous contributions to recent movements.

Looking Forward

From the Zapatistas of southeastern Mexico, who inspired global justice activists worldwide during the 1990s and beyond, to the landless workers of the MST in Brazil, and the scores of self-identified peasant organizations in some eighty countries that constitute the global network La Vía Campesina, people's movements in the global South in recent decades have challenged historical stereotypes and often transcended the limits of the possible. These grassroots efforts to reclaim the means of life, while articulating far-reaching demands for a different world, represent a starkly different relationship to both the present and the future than is offered by affluent activists and writers in the global North who either contemplate a catastrophic end to civilization, or urge us to go on consuming in the pursuit of a mythical individualist paradise.

Here in the North, new reconstructive movements have helped make visions of an ecological future far more realizable. At the local level, people are working to regenerate local food systems and develop locally controlled, renewable energy sources, sometimes in active solidarity with kindred movements around the world. Campaigns to create urban gardens and farmers' markets are among the most successful and well-organized efforts toward community-centered solutions to the climate crisis. In recent years, they have been joined in many areas by nonprofit networks aiming to more systematically raise the availability of healthy, local food for urban dwellers, especially those dependent on public assistance.[28] The local foods movement in the US, still significantly dominated by those affluent enough to seek out gourmet products, may be learning from Slow Food activists in Europe that it is necessary to directly support farmers and food producers, and aim to meet the needs of all members of their communities. As the food system is responsible for at least a quarter of all greenhouse gas emissions, such efforts are far more than symbolic in their importance.[29]

Community-based efforts to reduce energy consumption and move toward carbon-free energy systems have seen some important successes as well. More than two hundred cities and towns throughout the English-speaking world have signed on as "transition towns," initiating local efforts to address the parallel crises of climate chaos and peak oil. While the transition town movement sometimes tends to focus narrowly on personal and domestic-scale transformations, even avoiding important local controversies, the effort is filling an important vacuum in social organization, and creating public dialogues that more politically engaged and forward-looking efforts can build upon as the tangible effects of the climate crisis strike closer to home.[30]

Still, many chronically vexing questions remain. Can the potential for a more thoroughgoing transformation of society actually be realized? Is it possible for now-isolated local efforts to come together in a holistic manner and fulfill the old left-libertarian dream of a "movement of movements," organized from the ground up to radically change the world? Can we envision a genuine synthesis of oppositional and alternative-building efforts able to challenge systems of deeply entrenched power, and transcend the dual challenges of political burn-out and the co-optation of aspiring alternative institutions? Can a new movement for social and ecological renewal emerge from the individual and community levels toward the radical re-envisioning of entire regions and a genuinely transformed social and political order?

In these often cynical times, with ever-increasing disparities in wealth and media-saturated cultures of conspicuous consumption in the North, together with increased dislocations and imminent climate crises in the South, it is sometimes difficult to imagine what a genuinely transformative movement would look like. In the US, right wing demagogues appear to be far more effective than progressive forces in channeling the resentments that have emerged from continuing economic stagnation toward serving their regressive political agendas. But it is clear that when people have the opportunity to act on their deepest aspirations for a stronger sense of community, for the health of their families and neighbors, and for a more hopeful future, people's better instincts can triumph over parochial interests. This is a feature of community life that illuminates the entire history of popular social movements. It offers an important kernel of hope for the kind of movement that can perhaps reinvigorate the long-range reconstructive potential of a social ecological outlook.

A 2009 poll commissioned by the BBC confirmed that people in a dozen key countries agree that capitalism has serious endemic problems, and that we may need a fundamentally different economic system. Only in Pakistan and the US did more than 20 percent of those interviewed express confidence in the present status quo.[31] Perhaps this is the kind of sensibility that will reopen a broader popular discussion of the potential for a different kind of society. Maybe we don't need to resign ourselves to apocalyptic visions of the end of the world. Perhaps the climate crisis, along with the continuing meltdown of the neoliberal economic order of recent decades, can indeed help us envision a transition toward a more harmonious, more humane and ecological way of life.

6

Social Ecology and the Future of Ecological Movements

Today's grassroots climate movements are engaged in an epochal struggle to protect vital ecosystems and communities from the effects of an increasingly unstable global climate. While people in the global South and in indigenous and land-based communities worldwide face daily life-or-death confrontations with the forces of expanded resource extraction and exploitation, many Northern allies are still reluctant to act on their understanding that a global crisis is already upon us. Indeed, many advocates still limit their efforts to addressing the particulars of present-day energy and climate policies. As important as all of our detailed scientific and policy discussions may be in the near term, they scarcely begin to address the full scope of climate-related problems we face today.

Genuinely ecological solutions, on the other hand, will require us to see far beyond the political and economic arrangements that have led us to the present crisis. While public officials and many NGOs will continue to avoid any discussion that deviates too far from business-as-usual, those who embrace a longer-range, more holistic perspective need to actively explore the many paths-not-taken. There are no "easy solutions" to the global climate crisis, no instant policy fixes that will stem the tide of impending climate chaos. This is a serious obstacle. Where solutions are not readily apparent, people tend to focus on the obligations of their daily lives and avoid worrying about what may or may not happen in the distant future.[1] Over time, this can feed a sense of political apathy and despair about the future, fostering a climate that ultimately helps advance the false populism of the ultra-right. It doesn't have to be that way.

Throughout history, numerous forward-looking social movements have contributed to the positive transformation of society, and sustained their efforts over the long term, in times of change and stagnation, and of success and failure, by exploring the possible paths to a fundamentally different kind of society. Over the past half century of ecological activism, many have engaged in the search for a radical, counter-systemic outlook that can help transform our society's relationship to non-human nature and reharmonize our communities' ties to the natural world. One such perspective, which has played an important role in many forward-looking movements of the past several decades is that of social ecology.

The ideas of social ecology were largely developed by the philosopher and social critic Murray Bookchin, and have been elaborated by many others over the course of their development. Social ecology is viewed by most of its students and adherents as a holistic and evolving outlook that offers a critical and radically reconstructive perspective on ecological and social movements, both past and present. Social ecology encourages a searching historical and philosophical exploration of our evolving relationship to the rest of nature, and proposes a long-range vision of a world of self-reliant and highly interdependent eco-communities.

Numerous concepts that became common wisdom among ecological and progressive activists from the 1960s onward were first articulated clearly in Murray Bookchin's writings, including the socially reconstructive dimensions of ecological science, the potential links between sustainable technologies and political decentralization, and the evolution of the traditional politics of class on the left toward a more comprehensive understanding of social hierarchy in general. Social ecology is highly complementary to, and has learned a great deal from, indigenous world views, environmental justice movements, and practical ecological approaches to energy technology, urban design and permaculture. We will begin here by exploring some of Bookchin's core ideas, consider social ecology's contributions to a variety of recent movements, and then reflect on its continuing evolution.

The Outlook of Social Ecology

Bookchin's social ecology emerged from a time in the mid-1960s when ecological thought, and even ecological science, were widely viewed as "subversive." Even rather conventional environmental scientists were contemplating the broad political implications of an ecological world view, confronting academic marginalization, and raising challenging questions about the largely unquestioned dogma of perpetual economic growth. In a landmark 1964 issue of the journal *Bioscience*, the ecologist Paul Sears described his field of study as a "subversive science," and challenged the "pathological" nature of economic growth, inquiring whether ecology, "if taken seriously as an instrument for the long run welfare of mankind, would ... endanger the assumptions and practices accepted by modern societies."[2]

Bookchin carried the discussion considerably further, proposing that an ecological understanding of the world is not merely subversive, but fundamentally revolutionary and reconstructive. With the World Wars and Great Depression of the 20th century appearing to have only strengthened global capitalism, Bookchin saw the emerging ecological crisis as one challenge that would fundamentally undermine this system's inherent logic. His first book, *Our Synthetic Environment*, was issued (under the pseudonym, Lewis Herber) by a major New York publisher, Alfred A. Knopf, and cited by authorities such as the microbiologist Réne Dubos as comparable in its influence to Rachel Carson's *Silent Spring*.[3] *Our Synthetic Environment* offered a detailed and accessible analysis of the origins of pollution, urban concentration, and chemical agriculture.

In 1964, in a pamphlet titled "Ecology and Revolutionary Thought," Bookchin wrote:

> The explosive implications of an ecological approach arise not only because ecology is intrinsically a critical science—critical on a scale that the most radical systems of political economy

have failed to attain—but also because it is an integrative and reconstructive science. This integrative, reconstructive aspect of ecology, carried through to all its implications, leads directly into anarchic areas of social thought. For, in the final analysis, it is impossible to achieve a harmonization of man and nature without creating a human community that lives in a lasting balance with its natural environment.[4]

Over the next four decades, Bookchin's social ecology emerged as a unique synthesis of utopian social criticism, historical and anthropological investigation, dialectical philosophy, and political strategy. It can be viewed as an unfolding of several distinct layers of understanding and insight, spanning all of these dimensions, and more.

At its most basic level, social ecology confronts the social and political roots of contemporary ecological problems. It critiques the ways of conventional environmental politics and points activists toward radical, community-centered alternatives. Bookchin always insisted that environmental problems be understood primarily as social problems, and was impatient with the narrowly instrumental approaches advanced by most environmentalists to address particular issues. The holistic understandings of ecological science, he argued, require a social ecology that examines the systemic roots of our ecological crisis, while challenging the institutions responsible for perpetuating a destructive and irrational status quo. Bookchin was perhaps the first writer on the left to explicitly argue that an ecological outlook is fundamentally incompatible with capitalism's inherent drive toward unlimited growth and expansion.

This critical outlook led to many years of research into the evolution of the relationship between human societies and non-human nature. Both liberals and Marxists have generally viewed the "domination of nature" either as a fulfillment of human destiny and human nature or, in more recent decades, as an unfortunate but necessary precondition for the advancement of civilization. Bookchin sought to turn this view on its head, describing the "domination of nature" as a myth perpetuated by social elites in the earliest hierarchically-organized societies. Far from a historical necessity, efforts to dominate the natural world are instead a destructive byproduct of evolving social hierarchies.

Bookchin elaborated these ideas in his magnum opus, *The Ecology of Freedom*, a book described by the *Village Voice* in the early 1980s as belonging "at the pinnacle of the genre of utopian social criticism."[5] Bookchin closely examined the anthropological literature of the period, seeking forward looking principles and practices that emerge from our understanding of non-hierarchical "organic" societies. These core principles included interdependence, unity-in-diversity, complementarity, and the irreducible minimum: the principle that communities are responsible for meeting their members' most basic needs.[6] Complementarity for Bookchin meant disavowing the oppressive inequality of supposed "equals" within contemporary societies, instead invoking traditional communities' efforts to actively compensate for differences in ability among members. Bookchin's historical and anthropological investigations affirmed his belief that any truly liberatory popular movement needs to challenge hierarchy in general, not only its particular manifestations as oppression by race, gender, or class.

These explorations of the persistent role of social hierarchies in shaping social evolution and our relationships with non-human nature led Bookchin toward a philosophical inquiry into the evolutionary relationship between human consciousness and natural evolution. He sought to renew the legacy of dialectical philosophy—the philosophical tradition of transformation and becoming—abandoning popular oversimplifications and reinterpreting dialectics through examination of its origins in the works of philosophers from Aristotle to Hegel. Bookchin's "dialectical naturalism" emphasizes the potentialities that lie latent within the evolution of natural and social phenomena and celebrates the uniqueness of human creativity and self-reflection, even while emphasizing the emergence of human consciousness from the possibilities inherent in biological "first nature." It eschews the common view of nature as merely a realm of necessity, instead viewing nature as striving, in a sense, to actualize through evolution an underlying potentiality for consciousness, creativity and freedom.[7]

For Bookchin, a dialectical outlook on human history compels us to reject what merely is and follow the potentialities inherent in evolution toward an expanded view of what could be, and ultimately what ought to be. While the realization of a free, ecological society is far from inevitable, it may be the most rational outcome of four billion years of natural evolution. This dialectical view of natural and social evolution led to the sometimes controversial claim that nature itself can be viewed as an objective grounding for our social ethics.

Social ecology also proposes a distinct approach to political praxis, aimed at realizing the ecological reconstruction of society. Bookchin's "libertarian municipalism" draws on what he viewed as a fundamental underlying conflict between communities and the nation-state as well as on historical examples of emerging direct democracies from the Athenian *polis* to the New England town meeting. Bookchin sought a non-exclusive redefinition of citizenship and a reinvigoration of the public sphere, with popular assemblies moving to the center of public life in towns and neighborhoods, taking back control of essential political and economic decisions. Representatives in city councils and regional assemblies would become mandated delegates, deputized by their local assemblies and empowered only to carry out the wishes of the people.

Confederation is also a central aspect of libertarian municipalism, with communities joining together to sustain counterinstitutions aimed at challenging centralized power and advancing a broad liberatory agenda. In contrast to many ecologists who write about politics and society, Bookchin embraced the historic role of cities as potential sites of freedom and universalism, viewing the expanded practice of citizenship in empowered neighborhood assemblies as a means for educating community members into the values of humanism, cooperation, and public service.[8] The stifling anonymity of the capitalist market is to be replaced by a moral economy in which economic, as well as political relationships, are guided by an ethics of mutualism and genuine reciprocity.[9]

Libertarian municipalism offers both an outline of a political strategy and the structure underlying social ecology's long-range social vision: a vision of directly democratic communities challenging all forms of centralized power while evolving in harmony with the rest of nature. This vision draws on decades of research into political structures, sustainable technologies, revolutionary popular movements, and the best of the utopian tradition in Western thought. Bookchin spent his last decade intensively researching the history of revolutionary movements in the West from the Middle Ages to the mid-20th century, drawing out the lessons of the diverse, often subterranean, popular currents that formed the basis for revolutionary movements in England, France, the US, Russia, Spain, and beyond.[10]

Social Ecology and Social Movements

The influence of this body of ideas upon popular ecological movements began with the largely underground distribution of Bookchin's essays during the 1960s. Ideas he first articulated, such as the need for a fundamentally radical ecology in contrast to technocratic environmentalism, were embraced by growing numbers of ecologically-informed radicals. Bookchin and his colleagues, including Institute for Social Ecology co-founder Dan Chodorkoff, also participated in some of the earliest efforts to "green" cities and bring alternative, solar-based technologies into inner city neighborhoods.

By the late 1970s, social ecology was playing a much more visible role in the rapidly growing movement against nuclear power. As we have seen, rural communities across the US were being surveyed as potential sites for new nuclear power plants in the aftermath of the 1973 Arab oil embargo. The movement that arose to counter this new colonization of the countryside united traditional rural dwellers, and those who had recently moved "back-to-the-land," with seasoned urban activists, as well as a new generation of radicals who came of age in the aftermath of the ferment of the 1960s. Following the mass arrest of people who sought to nonviolently occupy a nuclear construction site in Seabrook, New Hampshire in 1977, decentralized anti-nuclear alliances began to appear all across the US. These alliances were committed to direct action, non-violence, and grassroots organization. Many were captivated by the utopian dimension of the emerging "appropriate technology" movement for which Bookchin and other social ecologists provided an essential theoretical and historical grounding.

New England's anti-nuclear Clamshell Alliance was the first to adopt the model of the "affinity group" as the basis of a long-range regional organizing effort.[11] Murray Bookchin introduced the concept of *grupos de afinidad*—borrowed from the Spanish FAI (Iberian Anarchist Federation)—into the US in an appendix to his influential 1968 pamphlet, "Listen, Marxist!"[12] Bookchin initially compared the revolutionary Spanish affinity groups of the 1930s to the countercultural collectives that were appearing in cities across the US during the late 1960s. Quaker activists advocated the formation of affinity groups as a structure for personal support and security at large demonstrations at Seabrook. But after the mass arrests and two weeks of incarceration in New Hampshire's National Guard Armories, participants began to view the affinity groups as the basis for a much more widely participatory, directly democratic form of social movement organization than had ever been realized before.

Bookchin's original "Note on Affinity Groups" was distributed widely in the lead-up to a planned follow-up action at Seabrook in June of 1978, and activists in Vermont, Boston, and elsewhere in New England worked hard to help the Clamshell Alliance live up to the most profoundly democratic potential of this organizational model. Anti-nuclear alliances across the US followed the Clamshell in taking their names from local species of animals and plants that were endangered by the spread of nuclear power, and adopted affinity groups and spokescouncils as their fundamental organizational and decision-making structures. While internal divisions would eventually undermine the affinity group-based internal democracy of this movement, Bookchin's writing significantly helped sustain the anti-nuclear movement's powerful utopian impulses. Meanwhile, annual summer sessions at the Institute for Social Ecology (ISE) in Vermont offered students some of the first intensive, hands-on experiences in organic gardening and alternative technology, combined with in-depth discussions of social ecology, ecofeminism, reconstructive anthropology, and other important political and theoretical topics that have significantly helped shape today's movements.[13]

From Green Politics to Global Justice

During the 1980s, social ecologists were intimately involved in the founding of Green political movements in the US and elsewhere. Many were inspired by the way in which the German Green Party emerged out of a variety of social movements, practiced a politics of grassroots democracy in its early years, and came to articulate a sweeping ecological critique in all areas of public policy, from urban design, energy use and transportation, to nuclear disarmament and support for democratic movements in Eastern Europe. But by the early 1990s, a growing tension had emerged between US Greens committed to a localist, decentralized approach, and those advocating for a national Green Party that would mainly run candidates for national office. As the US Greens began to splinter, social ecologists initiated a Left Green Network, many of whose policy positions were adopted at several national Green conferences. Those promoting a more mainstream agenda aggressively resisted this tendency, leading to many years of internal debates and divisions.[14]

Meanwhile, a group of recent social ecology students formed a youth caucus in the Greens, which eventually became an independent organization known as the Youth Greens. The Youth Greens attracted a significant base of young radicals largely from outside the Greens and joined with the Left Greens to initiate a major direct action to coincide with the twentieth anniversary of the original Earth Day in April of 1990. On the day following the official Earth Day commemorations—a Sunday filled with polite, heavily corporate-sponsored events—several hundred Left Greens, Youth Greens, ecofeminists, environmental justice activists, Earth Firsters and urban squatters converged on Wall Street seeking to block the opening of the New York Stock Exchange. Activists based around the ISE in Vermont had prepared a comprehensive action handbook, featuring a variety of social ecology writings and helped create a broad, empowering coalition effort. The next day, columnist Juan Gonzalez wrote in the *New York Daily News*,

Certainly, those who sought to co-opt Earth Day into a media and marketing extravaganza, to make the public feel good while obscuring the corporate root of the Earth's pollution almost succeeded. It took angry Americans from places like Maine and Vermont to come to Wall Street on a workday and point the blame where it belongs.[15]

During the 1980s and nineties, social ecologists also played a central role in the development and elaboration of ecofeminist ideas. Ynestra King's classes on ecofeminism at the ISE during the late 1970s were among the first to be offered anywhere, and annual colloquia on feminism and ecology were organized by Chaia Heller and other social ecologists throughout the early 1990s. Ecofeminist activists played a central role in initiating two Women's Pentagon Actions and a Women's Peace Camp alongside the Seneca Army Depot in New York State, while self-identified ecofeminists with a rather eclectic mix of political outlooks played a central role in the evolution of Green politics in the US.[16] While social ecologists became more skeptical toward ecofeminism *per se* as it evolved in a more cultural and spiritual direction during the 1990s, discussions of the links between ecology and feminist thought continued to be a centerpiece of the Institute's educational offerings.[17]

In the later 1990s, social ecologists played important roles in the rapidly growing movement to promote global justice and challenge the institutions of capitalist globalism, a movement that became an important precursor to today's climate justice movements. They raised discussions of the potential for direct democracy as a counter-power to centralized economic and political institutions, helped further the evolution of a longer-range reconstructive vision, and established grassroots democratic structures within the movement that came of age on the streets of Seattle in 1999. After Seattle, an ISE booklet titled *Bringing Democracy Home* highlighted the writings of various social ecologists on potential future directions for that movement. Global justice activists from across the US attended programs at the ISE in Vermont during the early 2000s to further their political analysis and join Bookchin and other faculty members in wide-ranging discussions of where the movement might be heading.

During the 1990s, Bookchin and his colleagues found themselves increasingly at odds with an anti-authoritarian youth culture that was increasingly fascinated with New Age spirituality, punk-inspired disdain for organization, and "neo-primitivist" notions of an impending "end of civilization." In response, Bookchin rose in defense of such unfashionable notions as reason, civilization, historical continuity, and the philosophical legacy of the European Enlightenment. Facing an increasingly hostile audience in anarchist-oriented activist circles, Bookchin cast aside his once-fervent hopes for reviving and updating the anarchist tradition. Encouraged by international colleagues, particularly in the Scandinavian countries, he articulated a new framework that he called "communalism," and redoubled his focus on the need for sustained political engagement and revolutionary organization.[18] Communalism, Bookchin argued, required a "new and comprehensive revolutionary outlook" drawing on the best of Marxism and the libertarian socialist tradition and rooted in an expansive view of confederal, municipally-centered direct democracies developing non-statist counterinstitutions capable of contesting political power. Speaking of his new communalist synthesis, Bookchin wrote:

> From Marxism, it draws the basic project of formulating a rationally systematic and coherent socialism that integrates philosophy, history, economics, and politics. Avowedly dialectical, it attempts to infuse theory with practice. From anarchism, it draws its commitment to antistatism and confederalism, as well as its recognition that hierarchy is a basic problem that can be overcome only by a libertarian socialist society.[19]

During the same period, the ISE's Biotechnology Project pioneered the use of New England's Town Meetings as a primary organizing vehicle to express opposition to the genetic engineering of food in the US. In March of 2002, residents in 28 Vermont towns voted for labeling genetically engineered (GE) foods and a moratorium on GE crops.[20] Eight towns took the further step of declaring a moratorium or otherwise discouraging the planting of GE crops within their town; in northern California, several counties outright banned the cultivation of genetically modified organisms in 2003-04. By 2007, 85 Vermont towns and 120 across New England had passed resolutions questioning genetically engineered agriculture. At a time when efforts to adequately regulate biotech products at the national level had become hopelessly deadlocked, this campaign invigorated public discussion of genetic engineering in the region and across the

US, gained international attention, and articulated a broader analysis of the social and ecological implications of genetic engineering and the commodification of life.

Justice, Freedom, and Technology

Two additional themes, first elaborated by Bookchin in *The Ecology of Freedom*, are also of potential interest to climate activists today. The first addresses the historical ambiguities that underlie the dual legacy of justice and freedom in the West; the second concerns the evolution of ideas about technology's role in society. The discussion of justice and freedom sheds light, for example, on a debate that arose among some activists in Copenhagen as to whether a justice-centered perspective— even the discussion of climate debts—could inadvertently bind activists to measures of value determined by the capitalist market. The discussion of technology arises in response to those who tend to view technological developments as the central driving factors in our social evolution.

In Bookchin's account, modern notions of justice began to emerge during ancient times, when a Greek-inspired cult of warrior elites was beginning to reshape social expectations and entrench patterns of exploitation, social coercion, and rule by privileged minorities. Whereas many traditional communities embodied an expansive sense of freedom rooted in reciprocity and complementarity, subjugated peoples had to settle for a more objectively neutral, nominally "blind" approach, relying on more limited standards of balance and equivalence.

Oppressed peoples have raised the banner of justice through the ages and have won countless epochal victories against elites who came to view themselves as naturally superior. Societies rooted in principles of justice are often less parochial and more inclined to accept strangers into their midst. At the same time, however, justice is often a poor substitute for the more expansive view of human freedom, rooted in an ethic of complementarity, which still thrives in many indigenous communities. Justice emerged, says Bookchin, "first, as a surrogate for the freedom that is lost with the decline of organic society," but "later as the ineffable protagonist of new conceptions of freedom."[21] Even as we struggle for justice in the present day, we can simultaneously strive to actualize our most far-reaching visions of a more fully liberatory society.

At the same time, climate activists and many others often hold to the view that new technologies, from agriculture to forms of warfare to the discovery of fossil fuels, are often the primary causes that impel the evolution of societies. Social ecology offers an important challenge to this view. Bookchin offers a compelling argument, supported by many other writers and historians, that technology is not an autonomous driving force nor an overarching principle of human evolution, but rather a reflection of its underlying "social matrix." Societies as radically different as the despotic Inca empire and the relatively egalitarian Iroquois confederacy had very similar, rather basic tools, yet these societies evolved in starkly different ways. As the historian Lewis Mumford has revealed, many technologies we take for granted today—from glass to waterwheels—had largely ceremonial or religious functions before they came to be tapped for productive or practical purposes.[22] For Mumford, the first "megamachine" was not technological in any sense, but rather the massive bureaucratic organization of human labor that built the Egyptian pyramids. Long before machines were invented to take advantage of centralized human labor, the earliest factories merely concentrated and intensified human labor, physically centralizing traditional practices such as spinning, weaving and dyeing that used to be performed at home.

Today's mega-technologies are not only products of the particular social relations of industrial capitalism, but were developed specifically to reinforce and strengthen those relationships. David Noble, a leading critical historian of technology, described in detail how the automation of machine tools after World War II was developed explicitly to disempower skilled labor and helped set the stage for a permanent war economy in the United States.[23] Similar concerns can be raised about many of today's advanced communication technologies, for example the surveillance techniques and software devices to convey our personal information to advertisers that are often embedded in the very structure of advanced web pages and mobile applications. From the design of our cities to the ways we use energy, the tools and technics that shape our lives are most often products of capitalist social relations, and have therefore served to reinforce and perpetuate patterns of hierarchy and rule. Rather than blame our social problems on technology, it is imperative that we work to envision a qualitatively different kind of eco-technology that helps us create a radically transformed, more humane and ecological society.

Social Ecology and the Future

In recent decades, a flowering of popular movements for land rights, for community survival, and against new land enclosures emerged throughout the global South. From the Zapatistas in Chiapas, Mexico to "water wars" in Bolivia and India, permanent land occupations by Brazil's Landless Workers' Movement (MST), and global resistance to corporate land-grabs, among many others, these movements have increasingly captured the imagination of global justice advocates, even those who for a time seemed to take environmental concerns for granted. These movements also offer a profound challenge to traditional environmentalism, as usually practiced in the North, and have challenged conventional approaches to land conservation as practiced by northern NGOs such as the Nature Conservancy and World Wildlife Fund.[24] While some authors have appropriately cautioned against the automatic labeling of indigenous, land-based movements as ecological, the resurgence of interest in these movements has furthered the evolution of many activists' ecological outlook.[25] It has also encouraged many thoughtful urban activists to broadly identify with the world views of those whose livelihoods are still principally derived from the land.

Today, with a growing awareness of climate disruptions and the profound social and ecological upheavals that we face, environmental politics may once again be ascendant. But often we see similar forms of narrowly instrumental environmentalism to those Bookchin critiqued in the 1960s and seventies. "Green consumerism," which first emerged as a widespread phenomenon around the 1990 Earth Day anniversary, has returned with a vengeance, incessantly promoted as the key to reducing our personal impact on the climate. Even some critical observers, such as the popular British columnist George Monbiot, have focused on the feasibility of a "least painful" lower-energy scenario, rather than posing a fundamental ecological challenge to the further destructive development of global capitalism.[26]

In this disturbingly constrained political and intellectual environment, what does the future hold? Will capitalism finally come to terms with the environmental crisis, perhaps driven by the dynamic movement to withdraw university and public funds from investments in fossil fuel corporations? Or are such campaigns mainly a step toward a more fundamental political challenge and a movement toward a thoroughly transformed future? To address these questions it is useful to consider some of the particular ways that social ecology may continue to inform and enlighten today's emerging social and ecological movements.

First, social ecology offers an uncompromising ecological outlook that challenges the entrenched power structures that underlie the systems of capitalism and the nation-state. A movement that fails to confront the underlying causes of environmental destruction and climate disruption can, at best, only superficially address those problems. Capitalism continually promotes false solutions such as carbon trading, geoengineering, and fracked gas as a "bridge fuel," which serve the system's imperative to keep growing. Ultimately, to fully address the causes of climate change and other compelling environmental problems requires us to raise long-range, transformative demands that the dominant economic and political systems may prove unable to accommodate. We can structure our activist campaigns in a manner that illuminates hidden structures of oppression and hierarchy, and reveals how various oppressions intersect, even while joyfully and dramatically illustrating the long-range, reconstructive potential of our movement.[27] Such a systemic approach can help guide our movements further in the direction of the social transformation that we know is necessary, challenge the continuing sellouts of corporate-friendly "official" environmentalism and help us "keep our eyes on the prize."

Second, social ecology offers us a lens to better comprehend the origins and the historical emergence of ecological radicalism, from the nascent movements of the late 1950s and early sixties right up to the present. Over five decades, the writings of Murray Bookchin and his colleagues have reflected upon the most important on-the-ground debates within ecological and social movements with passion and polemic, as well as with humor and long-range vision. Movements that are aware of their history, and comprehend the lessons of their many ebbs and flows over time, are much better equipped to discuss where we may be headed.

Third, social ecology offers the most comprehensive theoretical treatment of the origins of human social domination and its historical relationship to abuses of the earth's living ecosystems. Social ecology has consistently pointed to the origins of ecological destruction in social relations of domination, in contrast to conventional views suggesting that impulses to dominate non-human nature are a product of mere historical necessity. Social ecologists celebrate the ways that humans can participate meaningfully and supportively in the processes of natural evolution, rather than pretending that we can live as merely passive observers. Evolving eco-technologies, from permaculture to green urban design, can help point the way toward new relationships of harmony between our own communities and the rest of nature, prefigure new kinds of social relationships, and help us usher in more profound changes that reach beyond the local level.

Fourth, social ecology presents a framework for comprehending the origins of human consciousness and the emergence of human reason from its natural context. Bookchin's philosophy reaches far beyond popular, often solipsistic notions of an "ecological self," grounding the embeddedness of consciousness in nature in a coherent theoretical framework with roots in both classical nature philosophies and modern science. It advances a challenge to overturn popular acceptance of the world as it is, and to persistently inquire as to how things ought to be.

Fifth, social ecology offers activists an historical and strategic grounding for political and organizational debates about the potential for direct democracy. Social ecologists have worked to bring the praxis of direct democracy into popular movements since the 1970s, and Bookchin's writings offer an essential historical and theoretical context for this continuing conversation. When environmental organizations refuse to be accountable to their membership, we can offer a principled challenge, and also develop new forms of organization that help illuminate the potential for a fundamentally different kind of social and political power.

Sixth, at a time when the remaining land-based peoples around the world are facing unprecedented assaults on their communities and livelihoods, social ecology reminds us of the roots of Western radicalism in the social milieu of peoples recently displaced from their own rural, agrarian roots. Bookchin's four-volume opus, *The Third Revolution*, describes in detail how revolutionary movements in Europe from the Middle Ages to the Spanish Civil War were often rooted in pre-industrial social relations, an understanding which can serve to historicize and deromanticize our approach to contemporary land-based struggles. Rather than an exotic other, vaguely reminiscent of a distant and idealized past, current peasant and indigenous movements offer much insight and practical guidance to help us live better on the earth, reclaiming both our past and our future.

Seventh, social ecology offers a coherent and articulate political alternative to economic reductionism, identity politics, and many other trends that often dominate today's progressive left. Bookchin polemicized relentlessly against these and other limiting tendencies, insisting that our era's ecological crises compel a focus on the general interest, with humanity itself as the most viable "revolutionary subject." Social ecology has helped connect contemporary revolutionaries with the legacies of the past and offered a theoretical context for sustaining a coherent, emancipatory revolutionary social vision.

Finally, Bookchin insisted for four decades on the inseparability of oppositional political activity from a reconstructive vision of an ecological future. He viewed most popular leftist writing of our era as only half complete, focusing on critique and analysis without also proposing a coherent way forward. At the same time, social ecologists have often spoken out against the increasing accommodation of many "alternative" institutions—including numerous once-radical cooperatives and collectives—to a stifling capitalist status quo. Opposition without a reconstructive vision often leads to exhaustion and burnout. "Alternative" institutions without a link to vital, counter-systemic social movements are cajoled and coerced by market forces into the ranks of non-threatening "green" businesses, merely serving an elite clientele with products that are "socially responsible" in name only. A genuine convergence of the oppositional and reconstructive strands of activity is a first step toward a political movement that can ultimately begin to contest and reclaim political power.

Some defenders of the status quo would have us believe that "green" capitalism and the "information economy" will usher in a transition to a more ecological future. But, like all the capitalisms of the past, this latest incarnation relies ultimately on the continued and perpetual expansion of its reach, at the expense of people and ecosystems worldwide. From urban centers to remote rural villages, we are all being sold on a way of life that can only continue to devour the earth and its peoples. Today's high-tech consumer lifestyles, whether played out in New York, Beijing, Bangalore, or the remotest reaches of human civilization, defy all meaningful limits, ultimately raising global inequality and economic oppression to previously unimaginable proportions while profoundly destabilizing the earth's ability to sustain complex life.

The corrosive simplification of living ecosystems and the retreat into an increasingly synthetic world that Murray Bookchin warned of in the early 1960s has evolved from a disturbing future projection into an impending global reality. Today, our very survival depends on our ability to challenge economic and social systems at their core and evolve a broad, counterhegemonic social movement that refuses to compromise its values or settle for partial measures. Nearly fifty years ago, Bookchin observed and reported on the dramatic May-June revolt in Paris in 1968, when huge crowds of students and workers united to occupy the universities and the streets. One of their popular slogans, inspired by the writings of the French Situationists in the late 1950s and early sixties, is usually translated as, "Be realistic—do (or 'demand') the impossible." In response to the emerging ecological crisis, Bookchin urged his readers to consider a "more solemn injunction": "If we don't do the impossible, we shall be faced with the unthinkable."[28] Facing a future of unstoppable climate chaos if we fail to act quickly, we need to set our sights on nothing less.

Notes

Preface to the Revised Edition

1   *Climate Change Impacts in the United States: Overview and Report Findings* (Washington, DC: US Global Change Research Program, 2014), p. 9. Kevin Trenberth of the National Center for Atmospheric Research reports that atmospheric water vapor has risen by 4 percent since the 1970s, with a likely 5-10 percent effect on amplification of precipitation and storms: his article is "Framing the way to relate climate extremes to climate change," *Climatic Change* 115:2 (2012) pp. 283-29.

2   James Hansen, *et al.*, "Perception of climate change," *Proceedings of the National Academy of Sciences*, 109 (2012), pp. 14726-14727. Temperatures are defined as far warmer than normal here if they deviate from the norm by more than three standard deviations.

3   James Samenow, "February caps 29-year streak of warmer than normal months on Earth," *Washington Post online*, at http://www.washingtonpost.com/blogs/capital-weather-gang/wp/2014/03/19/february-completes-29-year-streak-of-warmer-than-normal-months-on-earth (March 19, 2014).

4   Pardeep Pall, *et al.*, "Anthropogenic greenhouse gas contribution to flood risk in England and Wales in autumn 2000," *Nature* 470 (2011), pp. 382-86.

5   Matthias Dietz & Heiko Garrelts, eds., *Routledge Handbook of the Climate Change Movement* (Oxford: Routledge International Handbooks Series, 2013).

6   Michael T. Klare, "The New 'Golden Age of Oil' That Wasn't," TomDispatch.com (2012), http://www.tomdispatch.com/blog/175601/klare_the_new_golden_age_of_oil_that_wasn.

7   For more details see Brian Tokar, "Tar Sands, Extreme Energy and the Future of the Climate Movement," in T. Black, *et al.*, eds., *A Line in the Tar Sands: Struggles for Environmental Justice* (Toronto: Between the Lines, 2014).

8   Subhankar Banerjee, "Shell Game in the Arctic," TomDispatch.com (August 2, 2012), http://www.tomdispatch.com/post/175577/subhankar_banerjee_arctic_shell_game; Clifford Krauss, "Shell Vessels Sidelined, Imperilling Arctic Plans," *New York Times* (February 11, 2013).

9   Tricia Shapiro, *Mountain Justice* (Oakland: AK Press, 2010).

10   See, for example, Marc Z. Jacobson and Mark A. Delucchi, "A Path to Sustainable Energy by 2030," *Scientific American* (November 2009), pp. 58-65, and further discussion of these issues in Chapter 5 of this book.

Global Warming and the Struggle for Justice

1   A thoughtful early response from US climate scientists to the widely publicized leaked emails from the University of East Anglia in the UK can be found at http://www.realclimate.org/index.php/archives/2009/11/the-cru-hack. For a thorough review of the scientific response to these allegations, see Michael Mann, *The Hockey Stick and the Climate Wars: Dispatches from the Front Lines* (New York: Columbia University Press, 2014), pp. 207-248.

2   On corporate funding of climate denial, see for example, *Koch Industries Secretly Funding the Climate Denial Machine* (Washington, DC: Greenpeace USA, March 2010), at http://greenpeace.org/kochindustries.

3   Anthony Leiserowitz, *et al.*, "Climate Change in the American Mind: Americans'

Global Warming Beliefs and Attitudes in January 2010," (New Haven and Washington, DC: Yale Project on Climate Change and George Mason University Center for Climate Change Communication, 2010), at http://environment.yale.edu/uploads/AmericansGlobalWarmingBeliefs2010.pdf.

4   Elisabeth Rosenthal, "Climate Fears Turn to Doubts Among Britons," *New York Times* (May 24, 2010).

5   Anthony Leiserowitz, *et al.*, *What's In A Name? Global Warming vs. Climate Change* (New Haven and Washington, DC: Yale Project on Climate Change and George Mason University Center for Climate Change Communication, 2014), p. 23.

6   David Leonhardt, "On Climate, Republicans and Democrats Are From Different Continents," *New York Times* (May 8, 2014), at http://www.nytimes.com/2014/05/08/upshot/on-climate-republicans-and-democrats-are-from-different-continents.html.

7   *IPCC Working Group I Summary for Policymakers* (September 2013), p. SPM-32, from ipcc.ch.

8   The emerging conflict between technocratic environmentalism and social ecology was first explored by social ecologist Murray Bookchin in the 1970s; several of his essays from that period are compiled in his *Toward an Ecological Society* (Montréal: Black Rose Books, 1980).

9   Andrew C. Revkin, "The Climate Divide: Reports From Four Fronts in the War on Warming," *New York Times* (April 3, 2007).

10 Kathy Marks, "Global Warming Threatens Pacific Island States," *The Independent* (October 27, 2006).

11 Nicholas Schmidle, "Wanted: A New Home for My Country," *New York Times* (May 10, 2009). An award-winning 2011 film, *The Island President*, further documented Nasheed's efforts.

12 Naomi Klein, "Rapture Rescue 911: Disaster Response for the Chosen," *The Nation* (November 19, 2007).

13 See, for example, Ernest Waititu "Drought Spurs Resource Wars," Pulitzer

Center for Crisis Reporting, reprinted in *The Indypendent* (New York City), No. 119 (April 25, 2008).

14 Jim Yardley, "Drought Puts Focus on a Side of India Left Out of Progress," *New York Times* (September 5, 2009).

15 Rahul Goswami, "The Road From Drought: The Monsoon Crisis of 2009," Pune: *InfoChange India*, September 2009, at http://infochangeindia. org/200909167941/Agriculture/Analysis/The-road-from-drought.html.

16 *No Place Like Home: Where Next for Climate Refugees?* (London: Environmental Justice Foundation, 2009), p. 4.

17 For further explanation see the Preface to this volume.

18 The various IPCC reports, and condensed "Summaries for Policy Makers," can be downloaded from http://www.ipcc.ch.

19 Reported in James Hansen, *et al.*, "Climate change and trace gases," *Philosophical Transactions of the Royal Society*, A 365 (2007), pp. 1925–1954 and James Hansen, *et al.*, "Target Atmospheric CO_2: Where Should Humanity Aim?" (unpublished manuscript), available from http://www. columbia.edu/~jeh1/2008/TargetCO2_20080407.pdf.

20 The IPCC's conclusions in this and the next two paragraphs are from their 2007 Working Group II Report, titled "Impacts, Adaptation and Vulnerability," and available from http://www.ipcc.ch.

21 IPCC Working Group II Report (2007), p. 393.

22 *Climate Change 2014: Impacts, Adaptation, and Vulnerability*, IPCC Working Group II Summary for Policymakers (March 2014), p. 12, from ipcc.ch.

23 For example, the IPCC's latest report mentions that the number of available citations on climate and health alone doubled between 2007 and 2009. See "Human Health: Impacts, Adaptation and Co-Benefits," Chapter 11 of the full IPCC Working Group II report (2014), p. 5.

24 World Resources Institute, *Synthesis: Ecosystems and Human Well-Being, A Report of the Millennium Ecosystem Assessment* (Washington, DC: Island Press, 2005), p. 119.

25 Juliet Eilperin, "New Analysis Brings Dire Forecast Of 6.3-Degree Temperature Increase," *Washington Post* (September 25, 2009), at http://www. washingtonpost.com/wp-dyn/content/article/2009/09/24/AR2009092402602. html; David Adam, "Met Office warns of catastrophic global warming in our lifetimes," *The Guardian* (September 28, 2009), at http://www.guardian. co.uk/environment/2009/sep/28/met-office-study-global-warming

26 See Mark New, *et al.*, "Four degrees and beyond: the potential for a global temperature increase of four degrees and its implications, *Philosophical Transactions of the Royal Society*, A 369 (2011), pp. 6-19.

27 *Human Development Report 2007/2008: Fighting Climate Change: Human Solidarity in a Divided World* (United Nations Development Program, 2007), p. 16.

28 *The Right to Survive: The humanitarian challenge for the twenty-first century* (London: Oxfam International, April 2009).

29 Rafael Reuveny, "Climate change-induced migration and violent conflict, *Political Geography* 26 (2007), pp. 656-673.

30 Praful Bidwai, "Climate change, equity and development—India's dilemmas," in Niclas Hällstrom, ed., *What Next Volume III: Climate, Development and Equity* (Development Dialog No. 61; Uppsala: Dag Hammarskjöld Foundation, 2012), p. 148.

31 Dan Smith and Janani Vivekananda, *A Climate of Conflict: The links between climate change, peace and war* (London: International Alert, November 2007), p. 3.

32 Michael T. Klare, "The Pentagon vs. Peak Oil: How Wars of the Future May Be Fought Just to Run the Machines That Fight Them" (2007), at http://www.tomdispatch.com/post/174810.

33 *Human Development Report 2007/2008*, p. 27.

34 Peter Baker, "Developing Nations Rebuff G-8 on Curbing Pollutants," *New York Times* (July 8, 2009).

35 "Hit the brakes hard," *Real Climate* (April 29, 2009), at http://www.

realclimate.org/index.php/archives/2009/04/hit-the-brakes-hard.

36 Malte Meinshausen, *et al.*, "Greenhouse-gas emission targets for limiting global warming to 2°C," *Nature* 458 (April 30 2009), pp. 1158-1163.

37 Richard Monastersky, "A burden beyond bearing," *Nature* 458 (April 30 2009), pp. 1091-1094.

38 IPCC Working Group I Summary for Policymakers (September 2013), p. SPM-20, from ipcc.ch; Meinshausen, *et al.*, "Greenhouse-gas emission targets for limiting global warming to 2°C," supra note 33.

39 Gwyn Prins and Steve Rayner, "Time to ditch Kyoto," *Nature* 449 (October 25, 2007), pp. 973-975.

40 Joeri Rogelj, *et al.*, "Global warming under old and new scenarios using IPCC climate sensitivity range estimates," *Nature Climate Change* 2 (2012), pp. 248–253; Glen P. Peters, *et al.*, "The challenge to keep global warming below 2°C," *Nature Climate Change* 3 (2013), pp. 4-6.

41 James Hansen, *et al.*, "Assessing 'Dangerous Climate Change': Required Reduction of Carbon Emissions to Protect Young People, Future Generations and Nature," *PLOS One* 8:12 (2013), p. 8.

The UN Climate Negotiations and Beyond

1   http://www.350.org/en/story, accessed April 2013.

2   Martin Khor, "Climate talks facing crisis," Shah Alam, Malaysia: *The Star* (June 15, 2009), via email.

3   Naomi Klein elaborated the link between Obama's renewed multilateralism and Europe's capitulation in "Obama isn't helping. At least the world argued with Bush," *The Guardian* (October 16, 2009).

4   Praful Bidwai, "Climate change, equity and development—India's dilemmas," in Niclas Hällstrom, ed., *What Next Volume III: Climate, Development and Equity* (Development Dialog No. 61; Uppsala: Dag Hammarskjöld Foundation, 2012), p. 158.

5   Lim Li Lin, "Why we need to save the Kyoto Protocol" (Penang, Malaysia:

Third World Network: November 2009).

6   Obama pledged that the US would reduce emissions approximately 17% from 2005 levels by 2020, echoing a bill that passed the House of Representatives in June of 2009, This was equivalent to only a 4-5 percent reduction from 1990 levels, the baseline established in Kyoto. EU countries, in contrast, agreed in Kyoto to an 8 percent reduction from 1990 levels by 2012.

7   Michael A. Levi, "Copenhagen's Inconvenient Truth: How to Salvage the Climate Conference," *Foreign Affairs* 88:5 (September/October 2009), pp. 92-104.

8   See, for example, I. Allison, *et al.*, *The Copenhagen Diagnosis: Updating the World on the Latest Climate Science* (Sydney: University of New South Wales Climate Change Research Centre, November 2009); on the British study, see David Adam, "Met Office warns of catastrophic global warming in our lifetimes," *The Guardian* (September 28, 2009).

9   Rachel Smolker, personal communication (December 9, 2007).

10   Full reports on these actions were posted at actforclimatejustice.org.

11   Becca Connors, email message from Friends of the Earth (December 18, 2009); George Monbiot, "Copenhagen Negotiators Bicker and Filibuster While the Biosphere Burns," *The Guardian* (December 19, 2009), at http://www.guardian.co.uk/environment/2009/dec/18/copenhagen-negotiators-bicker-filibuster-biosphere; Jeffrey D. Sachs, "Obama as Climate Change Villain" (December 21, 2009), from www.project-syndicate.org (accessed June 2010).

12   Martin Khor, "Climate: Talks end by only 'noting' an Accord after much wrangling," *South-North Development Monitor* No. 6840 (December 22, 2009).

13   Joeri Rogelj, *et al.*, "Copenhagen Accord pledges are paltry," *Nature* 464 (2010), pp. 1126-1128.

14   *ibid.* p. 1128.

15   People's Agreement, World People's Conference on Climate Change and the Rights of Mother Earth, at http://pwccc.wordpress.com/2010/04/26/peoples-agreement.

16   Martin Khor, "Complex implications of the Cancun Climate Conference"

Economic and Political Weekly 45:52 (Mumbai, December 2010).

17 Both are quoted in Anne Petermann and Orin Langelle, "The Durban Disaster," *Z Magazine* (February 2012).

18 Todd D. Stern, "The Shape of a New International Climate Agreement" (London, UK, October 2013), at http://www.state.gov/e/oes/rls/remarks/2013/215720.htm.

3. Toward a Movement for Climate Justice

1 Classic photos from Bali and subsequent UN climate conferences can be viewed in slides from an exhibit assembled by photojournalist Orin Langelle for the 2013 conference in Warsaw, at http://photolangelle.org/2013/11/09/the-warsaw-poland-exhibit.

2 "Mobilization for Climate Justice Open Letter to the Grassroots," at http://www.actforclimatejustice.org/about/open-letter-to-the-grassroots/.

3 CJA declaration, as conveyed via personal communication from Tadzio Müller (July 16, 2009).

4 Kenny Bruno, *et al.*, *Greenhouse Gangsters vs. Climate Justice* (San Francisco: Transnational Resource & Action Center, 1999).

5 *Toxic wastes and race in the United States: A national report on the racial and socioeconomic characteristics of communities with hazardous waste sites* (New York: United Church of Christ, 1987). The conclusions were updated in Robert D. Bullard, *et al.*, *Toxic Wastes and Race at Twenty 1987—2007: Grassroots Struggles to Dismantle Environmental Racism in the United States* (Cleveland: United Church of Christ, 2007).

6 Brian Tokar, "Environmental Justice," in *Earth for Sale: Reclaiming Ecology in the Age of Corporate Greenwash* (Boston: South End Press, 1997), pp. 125-140.

7 Available from http://www.ejnet.org/ej/principles.html.

8 Downloaded from http://www.ejnet.org/ej/climatejustice.pdf, accessed June 14, 2012.

9 Downloaded from http://www.ejnet.org/ej/bali.pdf, accessed June 14, 2012.

10 The climate-centered activities of GJEP are highlighted on their blog, at http://

climate-connections.org and IEN's at http://ienearth.org/climatejustice.html.

11 http://www.durbanclimatejustice.org/durban-declaration/english.html.

12 Climate Justice Now press statement, Bali, Indonesia, December 14, 2007, via Durban Group email list.

13 "Climate Justice Now: Principles of Unity," May 12, 2008 draft, via Climate Justice Now email list.

14 A full listing as of November 2010 is at http://www.climate-justice-now.org/category/climate-justice-movement/cjn-members (accessed August 11, 2010).

15 Statement of Henry Saragih, general coordinator of La Vía Campesina, to the Klimaforum alternative summit, December 7, 2009, via *CommonDreams. org*, accessed December 9, 2009.

16 J. Andrew Hoerner and Nia Robinson, *A Climate of Change: African Americans, Global Warming, and a Just Climate Policy in the U.S.* (Oakland: Environmental Justice and Climate Change Initiative, June 2008).

17 Rachel Morello-Frosch, *et al., The Climate Gap: Inequalities in How Climate Change Hurts Americans and How to Close the Gap* (Los Angeles: University of Southern California, May 2009).

18 WEACT's origins are discussed in Ashley Dawson, "Climate Justice: The Emerging Movement against Green Capitalism," *South Atlantic Quarterly* 109:2 (Spring 2010), pp. 325-326. Also see *Advancing Climate Justice: Transforming the Economy, Public Health and Our Environment: Conference Agenda and Resource Guide* (New York: WEACT, 2009).

19 Comments of Robert Bullard at "Advancing Climate Justice: Transforming the Economy, Public Health and Our Environment" conference, New York: Fordham University (January 30, 2009).

20 "What does Climate Justice mean in Europe? A Discussion Paper," via Climate Justice Action email list (March 26, 2010).

21 http://www.risingtidenorthamerica.org/about-rising-tide-north-america/our-history/, accessed June 18, 2012; "Remember, Remember: Climate Camp," *Shift Magazine* No. 12, at http://shiftmag.co.uk/?p=461.

22   See Brian Tokar, "Organization profile—Rising Tide," in Matthias Dietz & Heiko Garrelts, eds., *Routledge Handbook of the Climate Change Movement* (Oxford: Routledge International Handbooks Series, 2013), pp. 255-257.

23   Nicola Bullard & Tadzio Müller, "Beyond the 'Green Economy': System change, not climate change?" *Development* 55:1 (2012), p. 57.

24   Movement Generation's outlook and activities are described at http://www.movementgeneration.org. Their distinct approach to climate justice organizing, developed in collaboration with the Ruckus Society and other groups, is most fully explored in Hilary Moore and Joshua Kahn Russell, *Organizing Cools the Planet: Tools and Reflections on Navigating the Climate Crisis* (Oakland: PM Press, 2011).

25   Available at http://www.climate-justice-now.org/cj-in-the-usa-root-cause-remedies-rights-reparations-and-representation (accessed June 14, 2012).

26   See http://www.ourpowercampaign.org.

27   Jacqueline Patterson, "And the People Shall Lead: Centralizing Frontline Community Leadership in the Movement Towards a Sustainable Planet" (October 2013), via email.

28   Moore and Russell, *Organizing Cools the Planet* (supra note 24), p. 15.

29   See Anne Petermann and Orin Langelle, "The Durban Disaster," *Z Magazine* (February 2012).

30   GGJ's activities at the "Rio+20" environmental summit in Brazil in 2012 are outlined at http://ggjalliance.org/node/982. On climate justice and organized labor, see http://www.labor4sustainability.org and http://energydemocracyinitiative.org.

31   Patrick Bond, *The Politics of Climate Justice: Paralysis Above, Movement Below* (Durban: University of KwaZulu-Natal Press, 2012), especially pp. 188-194.

32   Rising Tide North America's sit-in at EDF's offices in Washington, DC in December of 2008 is described at http://www.risingtidenorthamerica.org/wordpress/2008/12/01/first-hand-account-of-environmental-defense-occupation; the November 30, 2009 demonstration at NRDC headquarters

is at http://www.risingtidenorthamerica.org/wordpress/2009/09/24/nyc-climate-activists-expose-the-true-"green"-of-big-enviros-deliver-giant-climate-"bill"-to-offices/.

33 La Via Campesina and ASEED Europe, "Call to the Climate Agriculture Action Day December 15th, 2009" (November 2009), via email.

34 Numerous such initiatives are described in detail in Tommy Linstroth and Ryan Bell, *Local Action: The New Paradigm in Climate Change Policy* (Burlington: University of Vermont Press, 2007).

35 Michael T. Klare, "The New 'Golden Age of Oil' That Wasn't," *TomDispatch.com*, at http://www.tomdispatch.com/blog/175601/klare_the_new_golden_age_of_oil_that_wasn.

36 See http://www.tarsandsblockade.org.

37 Mark Hertsgaard, "Climate Activists Put the Heat on Obama," *The Nation* (February 18, 2013).

38 "Uranium Hype Hits Indigenous Opposition Globally, Provokes Conflict in the North" (Ottawa: Mining Watch Canada, 2007), at http://www.miningwatch.ca/uranium-hype-hits-indigenous-opposition-globally-provokes-conflict-north; Ramsey Hart, "Indigenous Rights and Mining—Recent Developments, Opportunities and Challenges" (2011), at http://www.miningwatch.ca/article/indigenous-rights-and-mining-recent-developments-opportunities-and-challenges.

39 "What does Climate Justice mean in Europe? A discussion paper," supra note 20.

Carbon Trading and Other False Solutions

1 *Indigenous Peoples' Guide: False Solutions to Climate Change* (Bemidji, Minnesota: Indigenous Environmental Network and Carbon Trade Watch, 2009); *Hoodwinked in the Hothouse: False Solutions to Climate Change* (Hood River, Oregon: Rising Tide North America and Carbon Trade Watch (2011).

2 See, for example, *The Emperor's New Climate: Geoengineering as 21st Century Fairytale* (Ottawa: ETC Group, 2009).

3   Winona LaDuke, "Navajos ban uranium mining," *Earth Island Journal* (Autumn 2005), at http://www.earthisland.org/journal/index.php/eij/article/ navajos_ban_uranium_mining.

4   See, for example, Jan Willem Storm van Leeuwen and Philip Smith, *Nuclear Power: The Energy Balance*; available at http://www.stormsmith.nl.

5   Amory B. Lovins and Imran Sheikh, "The Nuclear Illusion," available at http://community.livejournal.com/greenparty/342794.html.

6   Linda Gunter, "The French Nuclear Industry Is Bad Enough in France; Let's Not Expand It to the U.S.," *AlterNet* (March 23, 2009); Peter Saunders, "More Trouble at Olkiluoto Nuclear Plant" (London: The Institute of Science in Society, March 2014), at http://permaculturenews.org/2014/03/06/trouble-olkiluoto-nuclear-plant.

7   John Kerry and Lindsey Graham, "Yes We Can (Pass Climate Change Legislation)," *New York Times* (October 11, 2009); Darren Samuelsohn, "Senate Dems Opening to Nuclear as Path to GOP Support for Climate Bill," *New York Times ClimateWire* (October 7, 2009).

8   See, for example, Emily Rochon, *et al.*, *False Hope: Why Carbon Capture and Storage Won't Save the Climate* (Amsterdam: Greenpeace International, 2008).

9   Trip Gabriel, "Ash Spill Shows How Watchdog Was Defanged," *New York Times* (February 28, 2014).

10   Charles Duhigg, "Cleansing the Air at the Expense of Waterways," *New York Times* (October 13, 2009).

11   Brian Tokar, "Biofuels and the Global Food Crisis," in Fred Magdoff and Brian Tokar, eds., *Agriculture and Food in Crisis* (New York: Monthly Review Press, 2010).

12   Lester R. Brown, "Supermarkets and Service Stations Now Competing for Grain," *Earth Policy Institute Update* (July 13, 2006), at http://www.earth-policy.org/Updates/2006/Update55.htm; C. Ford Runge and Benjamin Senauer, "How Biofuels Could Starve the Poor," *Foreign Affairs*, 86:3 (2007), pp. 41–53. A summary of the human rights impacts is in Brian Tokar, "Biofuels and

the Global Food Crisis" (*ibid.*). On the problem of global land grabs, see the chapter by the international research group GRAIN, "The New Farm Owners: Corporate Investors and the Control of Overseas Farmland" in Magdoff and Tokar, eds., *Agriculture and Food in Crisis, ibid.*

13 Ward Anseeuw, *et al.*, *Land Rights and the Rush for Land* (Rome: ILC, 2012), p. 4, available at http://www.cirad.fr/en/publications-resources/publishing/ studies-and-documents/land-rights-and-the-rush-for-land.

14 Jason Hill, *et al.*, "Environmental, Economic, and Energetic Costs and Benefits of Biodiesel and Ethanol Biofuels," *Proceedings of the National Academy of Sciences*, 103:30 (2006), pp. 11206–11210.

15 For example, see Joseph Fargione, *et al.*, "Land Clearing and the Biofuel Carbon Debt," *Science* 319:5867 (February 29, 2008), pp. 1235-1238; Timothy Searchinger, *et al.*, "Use of U.S. Croplands for Biofuels Increases Greenhouse Gases Through Emissions from Land Use Change," *Science* 319:5867 (February 29, 2008), pp. 1238-1240, both also available from www.sciencexpress.org.

16 See Rachel Smolker, *et al.*, "The True Cost of Agrofuels: Impacts on Food, Forests, Peoples and the Climate," (Asunción, Paraguay: Global Forest Coalition, 2008), especially Chapter 6, available at http://www. globalforestcoalition.org/img/userpics/File/publications/Truecostagrofuels. pdf; for continuing updates see http://www.nogetrees.org.

17 See, for example, ETC Group, *Who Will Control the Green Economy?* (Ottawa: ETC Group, November 2011), and Ronnie Hall and Joseph Zacune, *Bio-Economies: The EU's real 'Green Economy' agenda?* (London: World Development Movement and Transnational Institute, June 2012).

18 See, for example, Netherlands Environmental Assessment Agency, "Global CO_2 Emissions: Annual Increase Halves in 2008"; available at http://www.pbl. nl/en/publications/2009/Global-CO2-emissions-annual-increase-halves- in-2008.html.

19 An updated version of this history can be found in Brian Tokar, "The Myths

of "Green Capitalism," *New Politics* (Winter 2014) pp. 62-67.

20 R.H. Coase, "The Problem of Social Cost," *Journal of Law and Economics*, Vol. 3 (1960), p. 44.

21 J.H. Dales, Pollution, *Property & Prices* (Toronto: University of Toronto Press, 1968), p. 97.

22 W. David Montgomery, "Markets in Licenses and Efficient Pollution Control Programs," *Journal of Economic Theory*, 5 (1972), pp. 395–418.

23 Stephen Breyer, "Analyzing Regulatory Failure, Mismatches, Less Restrictive Alternatives and Reform," *Harvard Law Review*, 92:3 (1979), pp. 547–609.

24 For a more complete treatment of the origins of the US Acid Rain Program, see Brian Tokar, *Earth For Sale* (Boston: South End Press, 1997), pp. 33–45.

25 See, for example, Gar Lipow, "Emissions Trading: A Mixed Record, with Plenty of Failures," *Grist* (February 19, 2007).

26 George Monbiot, "We've Been Suckered Again by the US. So Far the Bali Deal is Worse than Kyoto," *The Guardian* (December 17, 2007).

27 Larry Lohmann, "Carbon Trading: A Critical Conversation on Climate Change, Privatization and Power," *Development Dialogue*, 48 (Uppsala: Dag Hammerskjöld Foundation, September 2006).

28 *ibid.* Lucrative offfset credits for HFC capture are often a perverse incentive for production to continue to rise.

29 Charles Forelle, "French Firm Cashes In Under U.N. Warming Program," *Wall St. Journal* (July 23, 2008); Fiona Harvey, et al., "Producers, traders reap credits windfall," *Financial Times* (April 26 2007).

30 Barbara Haya, *Failed Mechanism: How the CDM is subsidizing hydro developers and harming the Kyoto Protocol* (Berkeley: International Rivers, November 2007).

31 Lambert Schneider, "Is the CDM fulfilling its environmental and sustainable development objectives? An evaluation of the CDM and options for improvement" (Berlin: Öko-Institut, 2007).

32 For a more complete list of USCAP members, see http://www.us-cap.org.

33   See Hallie Boas, ed., *No REDD Papers* (Portland, Oregon: Indigenous Environmental Network and Carbon Trade Watch, 2013).

34   The details of the Waxman-Markey climate bill are best summarized in Climate Law Institute, "Analysis of Key Provisions of the American Clean Energy and Security Act of 2009 (ACESA), as Amended June 22, 2009" (San Francisco: Center for Biological Diversity, June 2009).

35   Marianne Lavelle, "Gore business: 2340 climate lobbyists," Center for Public Integrity (February 25, 2009), at http://www.politico.com/news/stories/0209/19255.html.

36   See J. Fargione, et al., "Land Clearing and the Biofuel Carbon Debt," and T. Searchinger, *et al.*, "Use of U.S. Croplands for Biofuels Increases Greenhouse Gases Through Emissions from Land Use Change," supra note 15.

37   Ryan Grim, "Internal Memo: Nuclear Power Company Could Make A Billion A Year From Climate Change Law," *Huffington Post* (June 23, 2009), at http://www.huffingtonpost.com/2009/06/23/internal-memo-nuclear-pow_n_219256.html.

38   John M. Broder, "With Something for Everyone, Climate Bill Passed," *New York Times* (July 1, 2009).

39   J. Kerry and L. Graham, "Yes We Can (Pass Climate Change Legislation)," supra note 7.

40   Ryan Lizza, "As the World Burns: How the Senate and the White House missed their best chance to deal with climate change," *New Yorker* (October 11, 2010).

41   Theda Skocpol, "Naming the Problem: What It Will Take to Counter Extremism and Engage Americans in the Fight against Global Warming," Cambridge, Massachusetts: Harvard University (January 2013), p. 5.

42   *ibid.*, p. 99.

43   Brad Plumer, "How the EPA's new climate rule actually works—in 8 steps," at http://www.vox.com/2014/6/4/5779052/how-to-figure-out-which-states-get-hit-hardest-by-obamas-climate-rule; David Hawkins, "Unpacking EPA's Carbon Pollution Proposal," at http://switchboard.nrdc.org/blogs/dhawkins/unpacking_epas_carbon_pollutio.html.

44   Larry Lohmann and Nicholas Hildyard, *Energy, Work, and Finance* (Dorset, UK: The Corner House, 2014).

On Utopian Aspirations in the Climate Movement

1   See, for example, Juliet Eilperin, "New Analysis Brings Dire Forecast Of 6.3-Degree Temperature Increase," *Washington Post* (September 25, 2009); David Adam, "Met Office Warns of Catastrophic Global Warming in Our Lifetimes," *The Guardian* (September 28, 2009).

2   Murray Bookchin, "Reflections: An Overview of the Roots of Social Ecology," *Harbinger*, Vol. 3, No. 1 (2002), italics in original.

3   See Fred Magdoff and John Bellamy Foster, *What Every Environmentalist Needs to Know about Capitalism* (New York: Monthly Review Press, 2011).

4   Alex Williams, "Buying Into the Green Movement," *New York Times* (July 1, 2007).

5   This case is made most comprehensively in Kate Gordon, *et al., Risky Business: The Economic Risks of Climate Change in the United States* (2014), a report commissioned by financiers Michael Bloomberg, Henry Paulson and Thomas Steyer, and available from http://riskybusiness.org.

6   Midnight Notes Collective, *Promissory Notes: From Crisis to Commons* (April 2009), p. 5.

7   For an insightful discussion of the capitalist trend toward financialization, see John Bellamy Foster and Robert McChesney, "Monopoly Finance Capital and the Paradox of Accumulation," *Monthly Review* 61: 5 (2009).

8   Van Jones, *The Green Collar Economy: How One Solution Can Fix Our Two Biggest Problems* (New York: Harper One, 2008), pp. 9-10.

9   Amory B. Lovins, *et al., Reinventing Fire: Bold Business Solutions for the New Energy Era* (White River Junction, Vermont: Chelsea Green Publishing, 2011) p. 235.

10   Mark Z. Jacobson and Mark A. Delucchi, "Providing all global energy with wind, water, and solar power, Part I: Technologies, energy resources, quantities and areas of infrastructure, and materials," and "Part II:

Reliability, system and transmission costs, and policies," *Energy Policy* 39 (2011) pp. 1154–1169, 1170–1190.

11   John Bellamy Foster, "The Jeavons Paradox: Environment and Technology Under Capitalism," in *The Ecological Revolution: Making Peace with the Planet* (New York: Monthly Review Books, 2009), pp. 121–128.

12   Richard York, Do alternative energy sources displace fossil fuels?" *Nature Climate Change* 2 (June 2012), pp. 441-443.

13   Matthew L. Wald, "Efficiency, Not Just Alternatives, Is Promoted as an Energy Saver," *New York Times* (May 29, 2007).

14   Uri Gordon, "Dark Tidings: Anarchist Politics in the Age of Collapse," in Randall Amster, *et al.,* eds., *Contemporary Anarchist Studies: An Introductory Anthology of Anarchy in the Academy* (New York: Routledge, 2009), pp. 249–58.

15   Derrick Jensen, "Beyond Hope," *Orion* (May/June 2006).

16   Richard Flacks, *Making History: The American Left and the American Mind* (New York: Columbia University Press, 1988), p. 7.

17   Karl Polanyi, *The Great Transformation* (Boston: Beacon Press, 1957).

18   Murray Bookchin, *The Ecology of Freedom* (Palo Alto, CA: Cheshire Books, 1982), pp. 43-61.

19   Randall Amster, "Anarchy, Utopia, and the State of Things to Come," in R. Amster, *et al.* (eds.), *Contemporary Anarchist Studies* (New York: Routledge, 2009), pp. 290–301. Emphasis in original; embedded references deleted.

20   Frederic Jameson, *Archaeologies of the Future: The Desire Called Utopia and other Science Fictions* (London: Verso, 2005), p. xi.

21   *ibid.,* p. 2.

22   Ernst Bloch, *The Principle of Hope*, Vol. 1 (Cambridge: MIT Press, 1995), p. 5.

23   Alain Touraine, "Society as Utopia," in R. Schaer, G. Claeys, and L.T.Sargent, eds., *Utopia: The Search for the Ideal Society in the Western World* (New York: Oxford University Press, 2000), pp. 18, 29. Touraine, once a pioneering scholar of social movements, now apparently prefers "moral individualism"

to political action as a means for limiting autocratic power.

24 Lyman Tower Sargent, "Utopian Traditions: Themes and Variations," in R. Schaer, *et al.*, eds., *Utopia*, p. 15.

25 *ibid.*, p. 14; Krishnan Kumar, "Utopia and Anti-Utopia in the Twentieth Century," in R. Schaer, *et al.*, eds., *Utopia*, p. 265.

26 Quoted in K. Kumar, *ibid.*, p. 266.

27 Immanuel Wallerstein, *Utopistics: Or Historical Choices of the Twenty-first Century* (New York: The New Press, 1998).

28 See Robert Gottlieb and Anupama Joshi, *Food Justice* (Cambridge: MIT Press, 2010); Mark Winne, *Closing the Food Gap: Resetting the Table in the Land of Plenty* (Boston: Beacon Press, 2008).

29 One study proposed that factory farming may be raising agriculture's contribution to global warming to as much as 50 percent: see Robert Goodland and Jeff Anhang, "Livestock and Climate Change," *WorldWatch*, (November/December 2009). For an overview of the links between agriculture and climate see Brian Tokar, "Food Sovereignty and Climate Justice," in Eric Holt-Gimenez, ed., *Food Movements Unite: Strategies to Transform Our Food Systems* (Oakland: Food First Books, 2011).

30 For an articulate political critique of the emerging "transition towns" movement, see Paul Chatterton and Alice Cutler, *The Rocky Road to a Real Transition* (Leeds: Trapese Collective, April 2008).

31 "Worldwide poll: Vast majority say capitalism not working," *The Raw Story*, (November 9, 2009), at http://rawstory.com/2009/11/survey-capitalism-not-working, accessed November 10, 2009.

Social Ecology and the Future of Ecological Movements

1 Yale psychologist Dale Kahan has demonstrated that people's views on climate correlate most closely with the views of their "cultural community," whatever their level of education: See his commentary, "Why we are poles apart on climate change," *Nature* 488 (August 16, 2012), p. 255, based on

a concurrent research paper, coauthored with six others, "The polarizing impact of science literacy and numeracy on perceived climate change risks," *Nature Climate Change* 2 (October 2012), pp. 732-735.

2   Paul B. Sears, "Ecology: A Subversive Subject," *BioScience* 14 (July 7, 1964).

3   René Dubos, *Man Adapting* (New Haven: Yale University Press, 1965), p. 196.

4   Murray Bookchin, "Ecology and Revolutionary Thought," in *Post-Scarcity Anarchism* (Berkeley: Ramparts Press, 1971), p. 58.

5   Quoted at http://essentialbooks.com/id50.htm.

6   Murray Bookchin, *The Ecology of Freedom* (Palo Alto, CA: Cheshire Books, 1982), especially Chapters 2 and 3.

7   The fullest elaboration of these ideas appears in Murray Bookchin, *The Philosophy of Social Ecology: Essays on Dialectical Naturalism* (Montreal: Black Rose Books, 1990; Revised edition 1995). For philosophical and scientific background to these ideas, see Hans Jonas, *The Phenomenon of Life: Toward a Philosophical Biology* (Chicago: University of Chicago Press, 1966).

8   Murray Bookchin, "A New Municipal Agenda," in *From Urbanization to Cities: Toward a New Politics of Citizenship* (London: Cassell, 1995), pp. 201–245. Also see his earlier *Limits of the City*, originally published by Harper & Row in 1974 and in an expanded edition by Black Rose Books.

9   Murray Bookchin, "Market Economy or Moral Economy," in *The Modern Crisis* (Philadelphia: New Society Publishers, 1986).

10   Murray Bookchin, *The Third Revolution: Popular Movements in the Revolutionary Era*, 4 volumes (London: Cassell, 1996, 1998; and Continuum, 2004, 2006).

11   At least one earlier mass action, aimed at shutting down Washington, D.C. to protest the Vietnam War in May of 1971, was organized on the affinity group model, but Clamshell activists were the first in the US to make this the underlying structure of their organization.

12   Murray Bookchin, "A Note on Affinity Groups," in *Post-Scarcity Anarchism* (supra note 4), pp. 221-222.

13 On the history and present activities of the Institute for Social Ecology, see www.social-ecology.org.

14 For more on the US Greens and the role of social ecologists, see Brian Tokar, "The Greens as a Social Movement: Values and Conflicts," in Frank Zelko and Carolin Brinkmann, eds., *Green Parties: Reflections on the First Three Decades* (Washington, D.C.: Heinrich Böll Foundation North America, 2006).

15 Juan Gonzalez, "Getting Serious about Ecology," *New York Daily News* (April 24, 1990).

16 See Greta Gaard, *Ecological Politics: Ecofeminists and the Greens* (Philadelphia: Temple University Press, 1998).

17 See Chaia Heller, *Ecology of Everyday Life: Rethinking the Desire for Nature* (Montreal: Black Rose, 1999); Janet Biehl, *Rethinking Ecofeminist Politics* (Boston: South End Press, 1991).

18 See Janet Biehl, "Bookchin Breaks with Anarchism," *Communalism* 12 (October 2007).

19 Murray Bookchin, "The Communalist Project," in *Social Ecology and Communalism* (Oakland: AK Press, 2007).

20 On the evolution of resistance to genetic engineering in the US, see Brian Tokar, "Resisting the Engineering of Life," in Brian Tokar, ed., *Redesigning Life? The Worldwide Challenge to Genetic Engineering* (London: Zed Books, 2001). For a more theoretical treatment, see Brian Tokar, "Biotechnology: Enlarging the Debate," *Z Magazine* (June 2001).

21 Bookchin, *The Ecology of Freedom*, p. 141.

22 Lewis Mumford, *Technics and Human Development* (New York: Harcourt Brace Jovanovich, 1967).

23 David Noble, *Forces of Production: A Social History of Automation* (New York: Oxford University Press, 1984).

24 Mac Chapin, "A Challenge to Conservationists," *WorldWatch* (November/ December 2004), pp. 17–31.

25 Larry Lohmann, "Visitors to the Commons," in Bron Taylor, ed., *Ecological*

Resistance Movements (Albany: State University of New York Press, 1995).

26   George Monbiot, *Heat: How to Stop the Planet from Burning* (Boston: South End Press, 2007). For a comprehensive review of more radical solutions to the climate crisis, see the "Less Energy" series in the Green politics journal *Synthesis/Regeneration* (now *Green Social Thought*), beginning with the Winter 2007 issue, No. 42 (Available at http://www.greens.org/s-r).

27   Chaia Heller, "Illustrative Opposition: Drawing the Revolutionary Out of the Ecological," in *Ecology of Everyday Life*, pp. 149–171.

28   Bookchin, *The Ecology of Freedom*, p. 41. Bookchin's more detailed account of Paris in 1968 can be found in a pair of essays, reprinted in *Post-Scarcity Anarchism* (supra note 4), pp. 249-270.